Get your stats in order with CGP!

Data, diagrams, standard deviation... there's a lot to grapple with in GCSE Statistics. But with this CGP book, you'll be a number-crunching expert in no time.

It's jam-packed with exam-style questions for every Higher and Foundation Edexcel topic, with the Higher Level questions clearly labelled. Every question has a worked answer, complete with mark scheme, at the back of the book.

We've topped it all off with a sprinkling of hints and tips to help you rack up an exam score that's well above average!

CGP — still the best! ☺

Our sole aim here at CGP is to produce the highest quality books — carefully written, immaculately presented and dangerously close to being funny.

Then we work our socks off to get them out to you — at the cheapest possible prices.

Published by CGP

Editors:
Will Garrison, Tom Miles, Andy Park, Caley Simpson

Contributors:
Andy Ballard, Sally Gill

Data used to produce the Holiday Destinations table on page 16 from the Office for National Statistics
and contains public sector information licensed under the Open Government Licence v3.0
http://www.nationalarchives.gov.uk/doc/open-government-licence/version/3/

Data used to produce the CPI data table on page 54 from the Office for National Statistics
and contains public sector information licensed under the Open Government Licence v3.0
http://www.nationalarchives.gov.uk/doc/open-government-licence/version/3/

Data used to produce the UK Average Weekly Earnings table on page 55 from the Office for National Statistics
and contains public sector information licensed under the Open Government Licence v3.0
http://www.nationalarchives.gov.uk/doc/open-government-licence/version/3/

Data used to produce the UK Population 2011 table on page 57 from the Office for National Statistics
and contains public sector information licensed under the Open Government License v3.0
http://www.nationalarchives.gov.uk/doc/open-government-licence/version/3/

Data used to produce the UK Deaths 2011 table on page 57 from the Office for National Statistics
and contains public sector information licensed under the Open Government License v3.0
http://www.nationalarchives.gov.uk/doc/open-government-licence/version/3/

ISBN: 978 1 78294 952 7

With thanks to Mona Allen and Glenn Rogers for the proofreading.
With thanks to Emily Smith for the copyright research.

Clipart from Corel®
Printed by Elanders Ltd, Newcastle upon Tyne

Based on the classic CGP style created by Richard Parsons.

Contents

☑ Use the tick boxes to check off the topics you've completed.

How to Use This Book..2
Exam Tips...3

Section One — Planning Data Collection

Planning an Investigation....................................4
Types of Data...5
Simplifying and Grouping Data..........................6
Data Sources...7
Populations and Sampling..................................8
Sampling Techniques...10

Section Two — Collecting Data

Questionnaires..13
Interviews..15
Observation and Reference Sources.................16
Experiments..17
Simulation...19
Problems with Collected Data..........................20

Section Three — Representing Data

Frequency Tables..21
Grouped Frequency Tables................................22
Two-Way Tables...23
Interpreting Tables...24
Bar Charts...25
Stem and Leaf Diagrams....................................27
Population Pyramids and
    Choropleth Maps...28
Pie Charts..29
Comparative Pie Charts....................................30
Vertical Line Charts &
    Frequency Polygons.......................................31
Cumulative Frequency Diagrams......................32
Histograms..33
The Shape of a Distribution..............................35
Scatter Diagrams..36
Time Series Graphs..37
Choosing How to Represent Data....................38
Misleading Diagrams...39

Section Four — Analysing and Interpreting Data

Mean, Median and Mode...................................40
Averages from Frequency Tables......................42
Averages from Grouped Data............................43
Measures of Spread...44
Measures of Spread — Grouped Data.............46
Standard Deviation...47
Standard Deviation from Frequency Tables....48
Box Plots..49
Outliers..50
Skewness of Data...51
Comparing Data Sets...52
Standardised Scores...53
Summary Statistics — Index Numbers.............54
Summary Statistics — Rates of Change.........56
Estimating Population Characteristics...............58
Estimating Population Sizes...............................59

Section Five — Analysing and Interpreting Diagrams

Interpreting Scatter Diagrams...........................60
Spearman's Rank Correlation Coefficient........62
Interpreting Correlation Coefficients................63
Time Series..64

Section Six — Probability

Probability...66
Relative Frequency and Risk.............................67
Expected and Actual Frequencies....................68
Sample Space Diagrams....................................69
Venn Diagrams and Two-Way Tables..............70
The Addition Law...72
Independent Events..73
Tree Diagrams...74
Conditional Probability......................................75

Section Seven — Probability Distributions

The Binomial Distribution.................................77
The Normal Distribution....................................78
Quality Assurance..79

Answers..81

How to Use This Book

- Hold the book <u>upright</u>, approximately <u>50 cm</u> from your face, ensuring that the text looks like <u>this</u>, not ſᴉɥʇ. Alternatively, place the book on a <u>horizontal</u> surface (e.g. a table or desk) and sit adjacent to the book, at a distance which doesn't make the text too small to read.

- In case of emergency, press the two halves of the book together <u>firmly</u> in order to close.

- Before attempting to use this book, familiarise yourself with the following <u>safety information</u>:

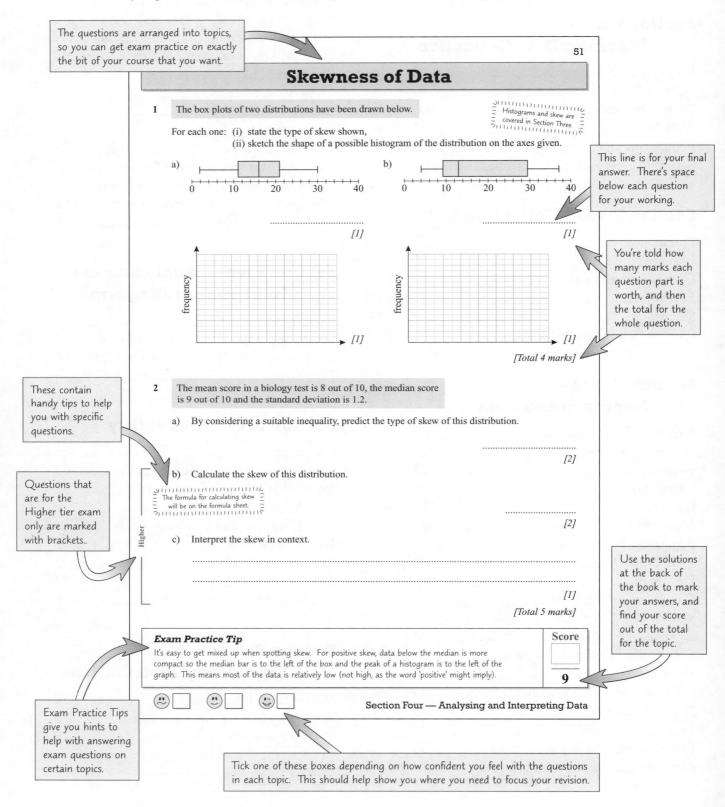

The questions are arranged into topics, so you can get exam practice on exactly the bit of your course that you want.

51

Skewness of Data

1   The box plots of two distributions have been drawn below.

Histograms and skew are covered in Section Three.

For each one: (i) state the type of skew shown,
                     (ii) sketch the shape of a possible histogram of the distribution on the axes given.

a)

b)

This line is for your final answer. There's space below each question for your working.

[1]

[1]

You're told how many marks each question part is worth, and then the total for the whole question.

frequency

frequency

[1]

[1]

[Total 4 marks]

These contain handy tips to help you with specific questions.

2   The mean score in a biology test is 8 out of 10, the median score is 9 out of 10 and the standard deviation is 1.2.

a)   By considering a suitable inequality, predict the type of skew of this distribution.

[2]

Questions that are for the Higher tier exam only are marked with brackets..

Higher

b)   Calculate the skew of this distribution.

The formula for calculating skew will be on the formula sheet.

[2]

c)   Interpret the skew in context.

[1]

[Total 5 marks]

Use the solutions at the back of the book to mark your answers, and find your score out of the total for the topic.

Exam Practice Tip

It's easy to get mixed up when spotting skew. For positive skew, data below the median is more compact so the median bar is to the left of the box and the peak of a histogram is to the left of the graph. This means most of the data is relatively low (not high, as the word 'positive' might imply).

Score

9

Exam Practice Tips give you hints to help with answering exam questions on certain topics.

Section Four — Analysing and Interpreting Data

Tick one of these boxes depending on how confident you feel with the questions in each topic. This should help show you where you need to focus your revision.

Exam Tips

Exam Stuff

1) You will have <u>two</u> exams. Each exam will last for <u>1 hour and 30 minutes</u> and will be worth <u>80 marks</u>.

2) You can use your <u>calculator</u> in <u>both</u> exams.

3) Timings in the exam are really important, so here's a quick guide...

> - You should spend about a <u>minute per mark</u> working on each question (i.e. 2 marks = 2 mins).
> - That'll leave about <u>10 minutes</u> at the end of each exam to <u>check</u> back through your answers and make sure you haven't made any silly mistakes. <u>Not</u> to just stare at that hottie in front.
> - If you're totally, hopelessly stuck on a question, just <u>leave it</u> and <u>move on</u> to the next one. You can always <u>go back</u> to it at the end if you've got enough time.

There are a Few Golden Rules

1) **Always, always, always make sure you <u>read the question properly</u>.**
   For example, if the question asks you to draw a vertical line chart, don't go and draw a bar chart.

2) **Show <u>each step</u> in your <u>working</u>.**
   You're less likely to make a mistake if you write things out in stages. And even if your final answer's wrong, you'll probably pick up <u>some marks</u> if the examiner can see that your <u>method</u> is right.

3) **Check that your answer is <u>sensible</u>.**
   Worked out that the probability of something is 27? You've probably gone wrong somewhere...

4) **Make sure you give your answer to the right <u>degree of accuracy</u>.**
   The question might ask you to round to a certain number of <u>significant figures</u> or <u>decimal places</u>.

5) **Look at the number of <u>marks</u> a question is worth.**
   If a question's worth 2 or more marks, you're not going to get them all for just writing down the final answer — you're going to have to <u>show your working</u>. <u>Longer questions</u> might need you to <u>explain</u>, <u>interpret</u> or <u>discuss</u> something, which means working out the stats and writing about what they show <u>in context</u>.

6) **Write your answers as <u>clearly</u> as you can.**
   If the examiner can't read your answer you won't get any marks, even if it's right.

> Obeying these Golden Rules will help you get as many marks as you can in the exam — but they're no use if you haven't learnt the stuff in the first place. So make sure you revise well and do <u>as many</u> practice questions as you can.

Using Your Calculator

1) Your calculator can make questions a lot easier for you but only if you <u>know how to use it</u>. Make sure you know what the different buttons do and how to use them.

2) Find out what <u>stats functions</u> your calculator has. E.g. if it can work out probabilities from a binomial distribution, use that function instead of calculating them yourself using Pascal's triangle (Higher only).

3) If you're working out a <u>big calculation</u> on your calculator, it's best to do it in <u>stages</u> and use the <u>memory</u> to store the answers to the different parts. If you try to do it all in one go, it's too easy to mess it up.

4) If you're going to be a renegade and do a question all in one go on your calculator, use <u>brackets</u> so the calculator knows which bits to do first.

> REMEMBER: <u>Golden Rule number 2</u> still applies, even if you're using a calculator — you should still write down <u>all</u> the steps you are doing so the examiner can see the method you're using.

Planning an Investigation

1   A pharmaceutical company wants to investigate whether their
new product is a better acne treatment than their previous product.

    a)   Suggest a suitable hypothesis for the pharmaceutical company to test.

      ....

      ....

           [1]

    b)   Describe one possible constraint of collecting data to test the hypothesis from part a).

      ....

      ....

           [1]

           [Total 2 marks]

2   Safia plans to investigate the distance travelled to school by students.

    Her hypothesis is:

         "The distance travelled to school by Year 11 students is greater than
the distance travelled to school by Year 7 students".

    Suggest three examples of other details Safia could include in her plan.
Give a reason why each of these details is suitable.
Your answer must include more than one stage of the statistical enquiry cycle.

> The stages of the statistical enquiry cycle are planning, collecting data, processing and presenting, interpreting, and evaluating.

    ....

    ....

    ....

    ....

    ....

    ....

    ....

    ....

    ....

           [Total 6 marks]

Exam Practice Tip

Being able to plan an investigation underpins everything you need to know for the GCSE statistics course,
so it's really important to learn the statistical enquiry cycle. If you're asked to plan parts of an investigation
there are loads of things you could say — just make sure you can support your ideas with a suitable reason.

Score

8

Types of Data

1   Two students, Anna and Ben, collected some data from their school.

Anna found out the star sign of each student in her class.

a)   State whether Anna's data is quantitative or qualitative.

....

[1]

Ben found out the number of students late to school one day. His data is quantitative.

b)   State whether Ben's data is discrete or continuous.

....

[1]

[Total 2 marks]

2   A music shop sells CDs, DVDs, tapes and vinyl records.

a)   Suggest one example of qualitative data that could be collected by the shop.

....

....

[1]

b)   Suggest one example of quantitative data that could be collected by the shop.

....

....

[1]

[Total 2 marks]

3   Martin investigated the popularity of rugby. He asked 50 people to rate rugby on a scale of 1 to 5, where "1" meant they strongly disliked it and "5" meant they strongly liked it.

Name the type of scale that Martin has used for his data.

....

[Total 1 mark]

4   Toby recorded the make and colour of the cars that passed his house in one hour.

Circle the **two** words below that best describe Toby's data.

bivariate   continuous   discrete   multivariate   qualitative   quantitative

[Total 2 marks]

Score:

7

Simplifying and Grouping Data

1 The table below shows the number of coins in the pockets of 100 people.

Number of coins	0-5	6-10	11-15	16-30
Frequency	44	26	19	11

a) Identify one lower class boundary from the table.

....

[1]

b) State the class width of the 0-5 class and the 16-30 class.

0-5 class width ....   16-30 class width ....

[1]

[Total 2 marks]

2 Ella recorded the ages of 30 people in a town centre. Her data is shown below.

42	13	3	31	15	20	19	1	59	14
8	25	16	27	4	55	32	31	31	10
32	17	16	19	29	42	43	30	29	18

a) Complete the table by grouping the data appropriately.

Age						
Frequency						

[2]

b) Give one advantage and one disadvantage of grouping the data.

Advantage   ....

Disadvantage ....

[2]

[Total 4 marks]

3 Kai measured the lengths of 20 bananas. He rounded the lengths
to the nearest 0.1 cm, then put the data in the table below.

Length (cm)	$14 \leq l < 16$	$16 \leq l < 18$	$18 \leq l < 20$	$20 \leq l < 22$	$22 \leq l < 24$
Frequency	2	4	9	4	1

The actual length of one banana was 21.98 cm before rounding.
Explain how rounding this length to the nearest 0.1 cm distorts the data.

*Try rounding the actual
length for yourself.*

....

....

[Total 2 marks]

Score:

8

Data Sources

1 State whether each of the students below are collecting primary or secondary data.

    a) Alice does an experiment to measure the heights of plants.

    ....

                                          [1]

    b) Carlos uses temperature charts from a national newspaper in a report.

    ....

                                            [1]

                                     [Total 2 marks]

2 Amir is investigating how a driver's age affects car insurance prices.

    a) Describe how primary data is different from secondary data.

    ....

    ....

                                          [2]

    b) (i) Give one reason why Amir might choose to collect primary data.

    ....

                                          [1]

      (ii) Give one reason why Amir might choose to use secondary data.

    ....

                                          [1]

                                       [Total 4 marks]

3 Julia collected data about the salaries of television presenters from the internet.

    a) Give two problems Julia might have when using data from the internet.

    ....

    ....

                                          [2]

    b) Explain why it might be difficult for Julia to collect primary data.

    ....

                                          [1]

                                       [Total 3 marks]

Score:

9

Populations and Sampling

1   Johanna is investigating the shoe size of students in her class.
    She asks every student in the class their shoe size.

    Circle **one** option below that best describes the method that Johanna uses to collect her data.

    sample frame   sample   survey   census

    [Total 1 mark]

2   Mia is investigating the incomes of people in a town.

    a)   Give one advantage of using census data instead of sample data.

    ....
    [1]

    b)   Explain why Mia might choose to use a sample rather than a census.

    ....

    ....
    [1]

    Mia uses the telephone book to randomly choose a sample of 100 people from the town.

    c)   Give one reason why this might not be an appropriate sample to use.

    ....

    ....
    [1]

    [Total 3 marks]

3   A football club is trying to find out about how much their supporters spend on merchandise.
    From the whole population of the town, the club sends a questionnaire to 1000 people
    chosen at random from the electoral register of the town.

    a)   Identify the population used by the football club.

    ....
    [1]

    b)   Identify the sample frame used by the football club.

    ....
    [1]

    c)   Give one criticism of the way that the football club have chosen their sample.

    Think about who the football
    club are actually interested in.

    ....

    ....
    [1]

    [Total 3 marks]

4 A scientist is researching the lifespan of deer in the UK.
She takes a sample of 100 deer from different locations in the UK.

a) Give one advantage and one disadvantage of the scientist using a sample.

Advantage ....

Disadvantage ....

[2]

b) Suggest one reason why it wouldn't be suitable for the scientist to use a census.

....

[1]

[Total 3 marks]

5 In a bakery, a sample of all the cakes baked each day are taste-tested.

a) Identify the population that the bakery uses for its taste-testing.

....

[1]

b) Explain why it wouldn't be appropriate for the bakery to do a census.

....

....

[1]

[Total 2 marks]

6 An environmental group is investigating the water quality of lakes in a county.
They use a map of the county to choose a sample of lakes to test.

a) Identify the sample frame used by the environmental group.

....

[1]

A journalist writes an article using the environmental group's results.
He uses the water quality of lakes in the county to predict
the water quality of lakes and rivers in the UK.

b) Is it appropriate for the journalist to do this? Give **two** reasons for your answer.

....

....

....

[3]

[Total 4 marks]

Score:

16

Sampling Techniques

1   Describe how to choose a simple random sample of 500 people from a list of 4000 names.

....

....

....

[Total 3 marks]

2   Describe how to use systematic sampling to select 50 items from a group of 700.

....

....

....

[Total 3 marks]

3   A textbook company has a list of all primary school teachers
in England and the school where they teach.

   a)   Describe how the company could use cluster sampling to choose a sample
       of primary school teachers for a survey.

       ....

       ....

[2]

   b)   Suggest one reason why they might use cluster sampling to choose a sample.

       ....

[1]

[Total 3 marks]

4   Erin and Mo collect data about the number of students in their school that wear make-up.

   Erin uses everyone in her next class as a sample.
   a)   Name the sampling method used by Erin.

       ....

[1]

   Mo uses a stratified sample that groups students into year groups.
   b)   Is Mo's sampling method appropriate? Give a reason for your answer.

       ....

       ....

[2]

[Total 3 marks]

5 A news reporter wants to interview fans of a local football team.
He chooses people who are wearing the team's football shirt to interview.

a) Name the sampling method used by the reporter.

....

[1]

b) Give one disadvantage of using the reporter's sampling method.

....

[1]

c) Explain why the sampling method used might be more appropriate
than simple random sampling.

....

....

[1]

[Total 3 marks]

6 Two market researchers are finding out opinions of a particular product.
They use different sampling methods to interview 40 people each.

Researcher A interviews 15 people less than 30 years old, 20 people aged 30 to 50 years old
and 5 people over 50 years old.

Researcher B interviews the first 40 people who pass the researcher.

a) Name the sampling methods used by Researcher A and Researcher B.

Researcher A: .... Researcher B: ....

[2]

b) Give one advantage and one disadvantage of using Researcher A's sampling method.

Advantage ....

Disadvantage ....

[2]

[Total 4 marks]

7 A company that makes springs wants to find out if springs from a batch of 5000 are faulty.

a) Describe how the company could use systematic sampling to check 100 springs from the batch.

....

....

....

[3]

b) Give one disadvantage of using systematic sampling to choose the sample.

....

[1]

[Total 4 marks]

Section One — Planning Data Collection

8 Fred is investigating people's opinions of public transport. He surveys a sample of 100 people passing through a bus station between 5.30 pm and 6.30 pm on a Monday evening.

Explain why Fred's sample is biased.

....

....

[Total 2 marks]

9 The weights of 50 cakes made in a bakery are shown below.

201 g	203 g	206 g	194 g	203 g	194 g	208 g	194 g	203 g	184 g
206 g	197 g	196 g	206 g	189 g	198 g	204 g	196 g	199 g	204 g
205 g	201 g	211 g	222 g	204 g	194 g	203 g	198 g	199 g	194 g
212 g	195 g	206 g	202 g	198 g	206 g	201 g	205 g	201 g	194 g
198 g	197 g	204 g	203 g	201 g	205 g	202 g	199 g	195 g	198 g

Use the random number table below to choose a simple random sample of 5 cakes.
Explain how you select the sample.

909	716	837	032
099	715	820	430
031	978	750	932
001	143	207	573

....

....

....

....

[Total 4 marks]

10 A sports club consists of 271 female golfers, 277 male golfers, 45 female swimmers, 38 male swimmers, 39 female tennis players and 18 male tennis players.
Each member only plays one sport. The club plans to use stratified sampling to choose a sample of 40 members, stratified by gender and type of sport.

a) Give one advantage of using stratified sampling to choose the sample.

....

[1]

b) Calculate how many members from each category should be chosen for the sample.
Write your answers in the table.

Start by working out the total number of members — you'll need to use this value in your calculations.

	Golfers	Swimmers	Tennis players
Female			
Male			

[5]

[Total 6 marks]

Exam Practice Tip

There are seven types of sampling to remember — simple random, stratified, systematic, cluster, quota, opportunity and judgement. Make sure you know their advantages and disadvantages and how to carry out each type. For Foundation level, you still need to know how to stratify by one category.

Score

35

Higher

Section One — Planning Data Collection

Questionnaires

1 Tabby has written the following question to try and find out about people's reading habits.

> On average, how many books do you read? Please tick one box.
>
> 1-5 ☐   5-10 ☐   10-15 ☐   >15 ☐

Identify **two** problems with this question.

....

....

....

[Total 2 marks]

2 Describe one problem with each of the following questions, and suggest a more suitable question that could be asked instead.

a) Do you spend a lot of money on Christmas presents?

....

....

[2]

b) Reality programmes are rubbish, aren't they?

....

....

[2]

[Total 4 marks]

3 A university wants to find out the occupations of its former students. They have a list of the former students' home addresses from when they were at the university. They decide to send a questionnaire to the former students in the post.

a) Give one advantage and one disadvantage of distributing the questionnaire to the former students by post.

Advantage   ....

Disadvantage   ....

[2]

The university asks the former students to return the completed questionnaire by post, but only 9% of the questionnaires sent out were returned.

b) Suggest two ways that they could improve the response rate.

....

....

[2]

[Total 4 marks]

14

4   Aaliyah wants to send out a questionnaire to all 900 students in her school to find out their opinions on the school facilities. Her teacher suggests she carries out a pilot study first.

   a)   Explain what is meant by a pilot study.

        ....

        ....

                                                                              [1]

   b)   Give two reasons why Aaliyah might want to carry out a pilot study.

        ....

        ....

        ....

                                                                               [2]

   c)   After carrying out a pilot study, Aaliyah decides that her question about what students think of the library needs an opinion scale. Design a suitable question that she could use.

        ....

        ....

                                                                               [2]

                                                              [Total 5 marks]

---

5   A health researcher is carrying out a study on the diet of secondary school students.

   Here is one of her questions:

| Toss a coin. If it lands on heads, tick 'yes'. If it lands on tails, answer the question below. |
| Do you eat at least one bar of chocolate every day?   Yes ☐   No ☐ |

   a)   Why is it suitable for the researcher to use a random response technique?

        ....

        ....

                                                                               [1]

   In a sample of 1000 students, 632 answer yes.

   b)   Use these figures to estimate what percentage of the students eat at least one bar of chocolate every day.

> You would expect about half of the students to get heads, so the rest of the students who ticked 'yes' are the ones who actually answered the question with 'yes'.

                                                                           .... %

                                                                               [3]

                                                             [Total 4 marks]

Higher

Score: ☐

19

Interviews

1 A magazine sends out an anonymous questionnaire which includes the following question:

"Have you knowingly broken the law in the last twelve months?"

Give one reason why it might **not** be suitable to use this question in a face-to-face interview.

....

....

[Total 1 mark]

2 A restaurant critic wants to find out people's opinions on eating out.

Give one advantage and one disadvantage of collecting information using a face-to-face interview, rather than using an online questionnaire.

Advantage   ....

....

Disadvantage ....

....

[Total 2 marks]

3 The government is carrying out a survey on income and family expenditure.
They consider three methods of collecting data from a widespread sample of households:

Method A: Send a questionnaire out by post to each household, to be returned by post.
Method B: Use a questionnaire in a face-to-face interview.
Method C: Use a questionnaire in a phone interview.

a) Give two advantages of using Method B instead of Method A.

....

....

....

[2]

b) Give two advantages of using Method C instead of Method B.

....

....

....

[2]

[Total 4 marks]

Score:

7

Section Two — Collecting Data

Observation and Reference Sources

1   Mavis is collecting data about the favourite sports of the students at her school.
    She asks her classmates what their favourite sport is and gets the following results:

10 people prefer football, 13 prefer rugby, 8 prefer tennis and 1 prefers BMX biking.

Design a data collection sheet based on these results for use with the whole school.

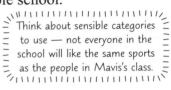
Think about sensible categories to use — not everyone in the school will like the same sports as the people in Mavis's class.

[Total 2 marks]

2   Kendra collected information on holiday destinations from the website for the Office for National Statistics (ONS). She finds the number of visits to the five most popular destinations by people in the UK, then rounds the values to 3 significant figures. She records her results in the table below.

Country	Spain	France	Italy	Republic of Ireland	USA
Number of visits (3 s.f.)	14 700 000	8 540 000	4 090 000	3 720 000	3 600 000

Source: adapted from data from the Office for National Statistics

a)   Give two potential problems with using data from the internet.

....

....

....

[2]

b)   Give one advantage of Kendra using this ONS data from the internet for her research.

....

....

[1]

c)   Kendra wants to compare the national results with data from her school.
     Design a data collection sheet she could use to collect this information.

[2]

[Total 5 marks]

Score:

7

Experiments

1 Milo wants to investigate the hypothesis "Listening to loud music makes people drive faster".

   a) Identify the explanatory variable and the response variable for this hypothesis.

   Explanatory variable: ....

   Response variable: ....

   [2]

   b) Write down two extraneous variables for Milo's hypothesis.

   ....

   ....

   [2]

   c) Explain why it is important to keep extraneous variables constant in an experiment.

   ....

   ....

   [1]

   [Total 5 marks]

2 A psychologist investigates how age affects the way children share toys by sampling children of different ages and observing them play with a selection of toys in her laboratory.

   Give one disadvantage of using a laboratory experiment for this investigation.

   ....

   ....

   [Total 1 mark]

3 A scientist is performing a psychology field experiment. He's investigating how people react to being asked not to use a door by an actor wearing either casual clothes or a uniform.

   a) Give one advantage of field experiments.

   ....

   [1]

   b) Give one disadvantage of field experiments.

   ....

   [1]

   c) Describe one extraneous variable that could have an effect on this experiment.

   ....

   [1]

   [Total 3 marks]

4 A teacher wants to know how much subject knowledge is forgotten by students over the summer holidays. He decides to carry out a before-and-after test on a group of 10 students.

a) Describe how the teacher could carry out his test.

....

....

....

[2]

b) Give one reason why the results of this experiment could be unreliable.

....

....

[1]

[Total 3 marks]

5 A doctor believes she has created a pill that will dramatically reduce patients' cholesterol levels in one week. She randomly splits her sample into two groups, A and B.
She records their cholesterol levels and starts an experiment. Every day for one week, she gives a real pill to each member of group A and a dummy pill to each member of group B.

a) Identify the experimental group and the control group in this experiment.

Experimental group: ....

Control group: ....

[1]

b) A colleague suggests that the doctor should repeat the experiment, this time using matched pairs. Explain what matched pairs are and how they are used.

....

....

....

[2]

c) Give one advantage of using matched pairs.

....

....

[1]

[Total 4 marks]

Exam Practice Tip

Lab, field and natural experiments all have different amounts of reliability and validity, depending on the amount of control you have. You need to know which one is most likely to be reliable and valid, but also why someone might choose not to use that method (i.e. the advantages and disadvantages of each type).

Score

16

Higher

Simulation

1   A table of 21 randomly generated three-digit numbers is shown on the right.

371	706	955	499	981	546	374
177	167	928	230	266	123	106
142	962	310	243	022	787	824

a)   Explain how these numbers could be used to simulate the results of spinning a five-sided spinner with sides numbered 1-5.

   ....

   ....

   ....

   [2]

b)   To win a game, you have to spin each of the numbers 1-5. Use the method you have described in part a) and the random numbers to estimate how many spins it will take to win the game.

   ....

   [1]

c)   Give one way in which you could improve the reliability of your estimation.

   ....

   [1]

[Total 4 marks]

2   A cinema currently has four films showing. The manager calculates the average number of people who go to see each film per day.

Film	Number of people
Superheroes!	42
Song of the Mermen	14
15 Days at Sea	13
The Devil's Confidante	31

Make sure you bear in mind the proportion of people who went to see each film.

The manager wants to simulate which film five random people will see. Explain how the manager could use the random number table on the right to carry out this simulation.

586	278	607	299
537	086	668	123
233	861	951	131

   ....

   ....

   ....

   ....

   ....

[Total 3 marks]

Score:

7

Problems with Collected Data

1   A travel agent asks his customers to fill in an online questionnaire when they return
     from their holiday. He thinks that older customers will have different travelling habits
     than younger customers. The first few results are shown in the table below.

Age	Country visited	Length of holiday	Average temperature
32	Egypt	1 week	34 °C
21	London	3 days	22 °C
190	Australia	20 days	30 °C
65	France	10 days	80 °F
48	Spain	26 °C	2 weeks
27	New York	5 days	

a)   (i)   Describe **three** ways in which the travel agent could clean the data.

     ....

     ....

     ....

     ....

                                                                                                              [3]

     (ii) Comment on the reliability of the data after the travel agent has cleaned it.

     ....

     ....

     ....

                                                                                                              [2]

b)   (i)   Give one problem with the method the travel agent has used to collect his data.

     ....

     ....

                                                                                                              [1]

     (ii) Suggest one way in which he could improve his online questionnaire to reduce the
           amount of data cleaning he will need to do.

     ....

     ....

                                                                                                              [1]

                                                                                              [Total 7 marks]

Score

7

Frequency Tables

1   Zoe plays in a pool league. She records how many of her pool balls are left
     on the table at the end of every game in a season. Her results are given below.

     3, 0, 7, 2, 1, 3, 1, 6, 4, 0, 5, 2, 0, 7, 3, 2, 1, 1, 0, 0, 0

a)   Complete the frequency table below for Zoe's data.

Pool balls left	0	1	2	3	4	5	6	7
Tally								
Frequency								

[2]

b)   How many games did Zoe play in total?

     ....
                                                                     [1]

c)   Players who have 5 or more balls left at the end of a game lose a point in the league.
     How many points did Zoe lose over the season?

     ....
                                                                     [1]

                                                            [Total 4 marks]

2   Farrah records how many birds she sees in her garden each day. Her results are given below.

     3, 8, 5, 7, 4, 3, 2, 6, 4, 7, 5, 4, 4, 6

a)   On how many days did Farrah record the number of birds?

     ....
                                                                     [1]

b)   Complete the frequency table below for Farrah's data.

Number of birds	0	1	2	3	4	5	6	7	8	9
Tally										
Frequency										

[2]

c)   State the modal number of birds seen.

     ....
                                                                     [1]

d)   Find the total number of birds seen.

     ....
                                                                     [2]

                                                            [Total 6 marks]

Score: [   ]

10

Grouped Frequency Tables

1 The ages (in completed years) of people leaving a film screening are recorded below.

85	86	98	18	12	10	28	28
29	35	36	85	86	98	18	25
6	7	7	8	12	10	13	12
10	11	14	13	13	10	8	15

There are a few ages that are much higher than the rest, so you should leave the last class open-ended.

a) Complete the grouped frequency table.

Age	Under 10				
Tally					
Frequency					

[3]

b) Find the number of people at the film screening who were at least 10 years old.

....

[1]

[Total 4 marks]

2 The times taken for 30 cars to reach 60 mph from a stationary start are recorded. The times given below have been rounded to the nearest 0.1 seconds.

6.0	7.7	7.0	5.5	5.2	8.4	7.6	6.8	8.5	7.5
8.9	5.4	5.5	5.1	6.5	5.7	8.6	7.1	6.2	5.8
5.7	6.1	6.9	5.4	8.6	7.6	6.5	5.6	5.2	6.6

a) Complete the grouped frequency table.

Time (t seconds)	$5.0 < t \leq 6.0$	$6.0 < t \leq 7.0$	$7.0 < t \leq 8.0$	$8.0 < t \leq 9.0$
Tally				
Frequency				

[2]

b) Find the number of cars that reached 60 mph in 7 seconds or less.

....

[1]

The actual time taken for the first car recorded to reach 60 mph was 6.043 seconds.

c) Explain how rounding the times can make the table misleading.

....

....

[2]

[Total 5 marks]

Exam Practice Tip

If you have to pick your own classes for the data, make sure they're sensible, don't overlap and cover the necessary range. For discrete data, the classes will have gaps and for continuous data there will be inequalities (and no gaps). It's a good idea to keep a tally row/column so you don't make any mistakes.

Score

9

Section Three — Representing Data

Two-Way Tables

1 The table below shows the heights (*h* metres) of fifty married couples.

		Women		
		$h \leq 1.4$	$1.4 < h \leq 1.8$	$h > 1.8$
Men	$h \leq 1.5$	5	2	1
	$1.5 < h \leq 1.9$	4	17	3
	$h > 1.9$	3	2	13

a) How many couples consist of men who are taller than 1.9 m and women who are taller than 1.8 m?

....
[1]

b) How many women are 1.4 m tall or less?

....
[1]

c) Mike says, "Tall men tend to marry tall women."
Comment on whether or not the data supports his statement.

....

....
[1]

[Total 3 marks]

2 A group of adults and children were asked to name their favourite colour.

a) Complete the table to show the data.

	Black	Red	Yellow	Green	Total
Adults	6	2		3	11
Children	1		3		
Total		9		6	

[2]

b) Find the number of people whose favourite colour is yellow or green.

....
[1]

c) Find the number of children whose favourite colour is **not** black.

....
[1]

[Total 4 marks]

Score: ☐

7

Section Three — Representing Data

Interpreting Tables

1   A pet shop owner records the percentage of each type of animal sold in the table below.

Animal	2015	2016	2017	2018
Rabbit	40.7%	48.9%	55.2%	55.3%
Rat	18.0%	15.2%	17.2%	16.6%
Guinea Pig	26.9%	22.8%	14.8%	18.4%
Snake	12.0%	9.8%	4.9%	4.1%
Other	2.4%	3.3%	7.9%	5.5%

a)   What was the most popular animal sold in 2016?

....

[1]

b)   The percentages for 2018 don't add up to 100%. Give one possible reason for this.

....

[1]

[Total 2 marks]

2   The table below shows the number of hours flown by oil rig support helicopters from 1995 to 2014 by helicopter type. The data is in 1000s of hours.

Helicopter Type	Year			
	1995-1999	2000-2004	2005-2009	2010-2014
A	80	70	90	90
B	160	150	160	130
C	200	260	300	300
D	70	110	120	150
E	80	50	40	60
F	90	70	70	80
All Helicopters	680	710		

a)   Complete the total row in the table.

[1]

b)   Describe the trend in total flying hours between 1995 and 2014 for all helicopters.

....

[1]

c)   10.3% of the 1995-1999 flying hours were flown by Type D helicopters.
     Compare this to the proportion of hours flown by Type D helicopters in the period 2010-2014.

....

....

[2]

[Total 4 marks]

Score:

6

Bar Charts

1 The incomplete pictogram below shows the number of books borrowed from a mobile library over five days.

Monday	▭ ▭ ▭
Tuesday	▭ ▭
Wednesday	▭ ▭ ▭ ▭
Thursday	▭ ▭ ▭
Friday	

Key: ▭ = 2 books

a) How many books were borrowed on Thursday?

....

[1]

b) How many more books were borrowed on Wednesday than Tuesday?

....

[1]

c) Seven books were borrowed on Friday. Complete the pictogram.

[1]

d) On one day, the number of books borrowed was half the number of books borrowed on Monday. Which day was this?

....

[1]

[Total 4 marks]

2 The composite bar charts below show the marital status for males and females aged over 65 years old in a town.

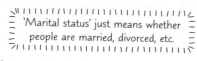
'Marital status' just means whether people are married, divorced, etc.

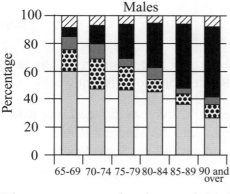
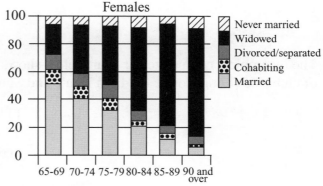

a) What percentage of males aged 65-69 are married?

.... %

[1]

b) Which marital status is most common amongst women aged 85-89?

....

[1]

c) Pierre says "There are more married men aged 65-69 than there are married women aged 65-69 in the town." Explain why Pierre may be wrong.

....

[1]

[Total 3 marks]

Section Three — Representing Data

3   The multiple bar chart shows the number of people of each sex that smoke in a city by year.

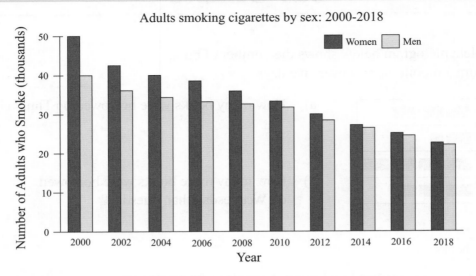

Adults smoking cigarettes by sex: 2000-2018

a)   Describe the overall trend in smoking habits from 2000 to 2018.

....

[1]

b)   Find the difference between the numbers of men and women smoking in 2000.

....

[1]

c)   Describe how this difference appears to be changing over the years.

....

[1]

[Total 3 marks]

4   The incomplete composite bar chart below shows the number of cyclists on each type of club ride (Long Route, Medium Route and Short Route) for two different weeks.

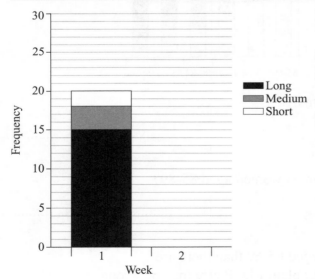

In Week 2, 12 cyclists did the Long Route,
15 cyclists did the Medium Route
and 3 cyclists did the Short Route.

a)   Complete the composite bar chart for Week 2.

[2]

b)   Suggest one reason why it's appropriate
to show this data on a composite bar chart.

....

....

....

[1]

[Total 3 marks]

Score:

13

Section Three — Representing Data

Stem and Leaf Diagrams

1   The scores of 16 children who took a maths test (out of 70) are given below.

48, 44, 37, 66, 70, 52, 31, 50, 45, 52, 45, 43, 32, 45, 59, 61

a)   Draw a stem and leaf diagram to show the data.

Stem and leaf diagrams should always have a key.

[3]

b)   State the modal score.

....

[1]

c)   Find the range of the scores.

....

[1]

[Total 5 marks]

2   Sven and Igor record the length of each track (in minutes : seconds) on their favourite albums. Sven's data is shown on the stem and leaf diagram below.

		Sven	Igor
Key: 10|2 = 2:10	12 10	2	
	50 32 18 12 06	3	
	53 51 15 15	4	
	31	5	

Igor's data is listed below:

4:10, 4:48, 5:25, 2:50, 3:24, 4:10, 5:32, 5:21, 4:34, 3:16, 4:50

a)   Complete the stem and leaf diagram for Igor's data.

[2]

b)   Find the median of Sven's data.

....

[2]

c)   Whose tracks are generally longer? Give a reason for your answer.

....

....

[2]

[Total 6 marks]

Score:

11

Section Three — Representing Data

Population Pyramids and Choropleth Maps

1   An area of a town is divided into 25 equal squares. The number of people living in each region represented by a square is recorded and shown on the choropleth map below.

Which part of the choropleth map shows the highest number of people? Explain your answer.

....

....

....

[Total 2 marks]

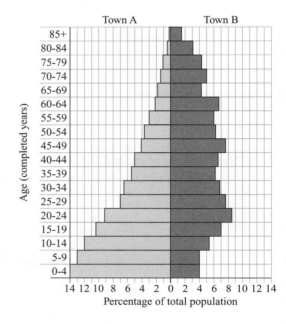

2   The population pyramid on the right shows the ages of people in two towns, A and B.

a)   Find the percentage of people in Town A who are under 15.

.... %

[1]

b)   The percentage of one age group in Town B is double the percentage of the same age group in Town A. Which age group is this?

....

[1]

c)   Suggest one reason why there is a difference between the proportions of people over the age of 70 in Town A and Town B.

....

[1]

d)   Which town is most likely to have had a higher birth rate in the last 10 years? Explain your answer.

....

....

For part d), think about what the proportion of younger people in the towns suggests about their birth rate.

[2]

[Total 5 marks]

Exam Practice Tip

Population pyramids can look complicated, but remember they're just two bar charts that are back-to-back. The shape of the distribution tells you about birth rates, death rates and life expectancy of the population — e.g. an 'inverted pyramid' suggests there's a low birth rate, low death rate and long life expectancy.

Score

7

Pie Charts

1   The shirt colour of 45 students was recorded and put in the table below.
Draw a pie chart with a radius of 1.5 cm to show this data.

Colour	Frequency
Red	3
Blue	12
Green	10
Black	5
Other	15

[Total 4 marks]

2   The condition of a sample of 960 bananas from a warehouse is recorded.

a)   Use the pie chart below to complete the table. Show your working.

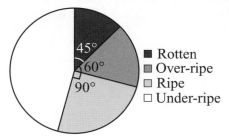

Condition	Frequency
Rotten	
Over-ripe	
Ripe	
Under-ripe	

[3]

The diagrams below show the condition of a sample of oranges and apples from the warehouse.

Oranges

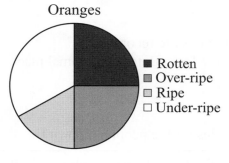

Apples

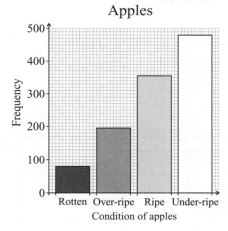

b)   Johnny says that there were more rotten oranges than rotten apples.
Explain whether or not the two diagrams support Johnny's statement.

....

....

....

[2]

[Total 5 marks]

Score: ☐

9

 ☐   ☐   ☐

Section Three — Representing Data

Comparative Pie Charts

1 The pie charts show how Jin and Tony spent their pocket money one month. Jin spent £30 and Tony spent £50.

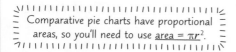

□ = Food
□ = Music
■ = Clothes
■ = Books

a) Who spent more money on music?

....
[1]

b) If the diameter of Jin's pie chart is 3 cm, find the radius of Tony's pie chart.

> Comparative pie charts have proportional areas, so you'll need to use <u>area = πr^2</u>.

[3]

[Total 4 marks]

2 The pie chart below shows information about the distances travelled to work (*d* km) by people in Town A in 2018. It represents 2880 people and has a radius of 2 cm.

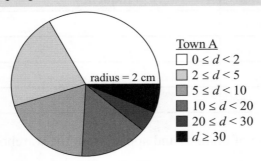

radius = 2 cm

Town A
□ $0 \le d < 2$
□ $2 \le d < 5$
■ $5 \le d < 10$
■ $10 \le d < 20$
■ $20 \le d < 30$
■ $d \ge 30$

a) The distances travelled to work by 3420 people in Town B are recorded.
   (i) Calculate the radius of a comparative pie chart for Town B, to one decimal place.

[3]

   (ii) Complete the table below by calculating the angles for the people in Town B.

Distance (*d* km)	$0 \le d < 2$	$2 \le d < 5$	$5 \le d < 10$	$10 \le d < 20$	$20 \le d < 30$	$d \ge 30$
Frequency	1273	608	532	475	247	285
Angle (degrees)						

[2]

   (iii) Draw the comparative pie chart for Town B next to the pie chart for Town A.

[2]

b) Give one similarity and one difference between the Town A and Town B data.

....

....

[2]

[Total 9 marks]

Score:

13

Vertical Line Charts & Frequency Polygons

1   Charlie recorded the number of plants in all the offices at her workplace in the table below.

   a)   Draw a vertical line chart to show
         Charlie's data.

Number of plants	1	2	3	4	5
Frequency	1	2	5	3	1

                                                                                        [2]

   b)   Explain why it would **not** be suitable to show the plants' heights on a vertical line chart.

         ....
                                                                                        [1]

                                                                            [Total 3 marks]

2   Anna records the heights (x cm) of players on two school football teams in the table below.

Height (x cm)	$150 \leq x < 160$	$160 \leq x < 170$	$170 \leq x < 180$	$180 \leq x < 190$	$190 \leq x < 200$
Team A	0	1	2	7	1
Team B	1	4	5	1	0

Anna shows her results for Team A on this frequency polygon:

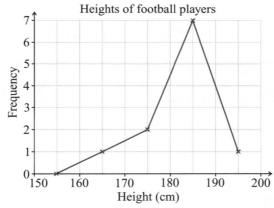

   a)   Complete the graph by showing the results for Team B on the same axes.

                                                                                        [2]

   b)   Anna says that the players on Team A are generally taller than those on Team B.
         Explain how the frequency polygon supports this view.

         ....
                                                                                        [1]

                                                                            [Total 3 marks]

Exam Practice Tip

To draw a frequency polygon, you plot the frequencies at the midpoint of each class and use straight lines to join the points. They can be open or closed, depending on whether lines join the polygon to the x-axis where the next (imaginary) class midpoint would be — e.g. the frequency polygon for Team A above is open.

Score

6

                                        Section Three — Representing Data

Cumulative Frequency Diagrams

1 Wolfgang records the number of words in each sentence of a newspaper article in the table below.

Number of words	5	6	7	8	9	10	11
Frequency	2	5	6	3	2	1	1
Cumulative frequency			.				

a) Complete the table by filling in the cumulative frequency row.

[2]

b) Draw a cumulative frequency step polygon to show Wolfgang's data.

[2]

c) Find the number of sentences that had 10 or fewer words in them.

....

[1]

[Total 5 marks]

2 The times taken (*t* minutes) by 11 different kettles to boil a litre of water are shown in the table.

Time taken (*t* minutes)	$1.5 \le t < 2$	$2 \le t < 2.5$	$2.5 \le t < 3$	$3 \le t < 3.5$	$3.5 \le t < 4$
Frequency	1	4	5	1	0

a) Draw a cumulative frequency graph to show the data.

Remember — for a cumulative frequency graph you should plot the cumulative frequency against the upper boundary for each interval.

[4]

b) Estimate the number of kettles that took more than 2.25 minutes to boil the water.

....

[2]

[Total 6 marks]

Score:

11

Section Three — Representing Data

Histograms

1 The histogram below shows the average speed (*s* km/h) of 200 cyclists in a race.

25 cyclists had an average speed of $30 < s \leq 35$ km/h.
Use the histogram to complete the table.

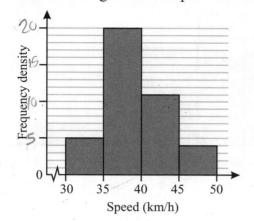

Speed (*s* km/h)	Frequency density	Density
$30 < s \leq 35$	25	5
$35 < s \leq 40$	100	20
$40 < s \leq 45$	50	10
$45 < s \leq 50$	25	5

[Total 2 marks]

2 Anika measures the length (*l* cm) of 20 butterflies at a butterfly sanctuary.
She records the lengths in the table below.

Length (*l* cm)	$0 < l \leq 4$	$4 < l \leq 8$	$8 < l \leq 12$	$12 < l \leq 16$	$16 < l \leq 20$
Frequency	3	7	4	5	1
FD	0.75	1.75	1	1.25	0.25

a) Explain why it is appropriate to use a histogram to show Anika's data.

..........Because she uses grouped data...

[1]

b) Draw a histogram on the axes below to show Anika's data.

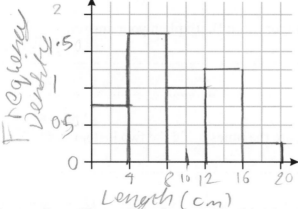

[3]

c) (i) Estimate the number of butterflies that measured between 10 and 16 cm.

need find out how to do interpolation ....

[2]

(ii) Explain why your answer to part (i) is an estimate.

....

[1]

[Total 7 marks]

Section Three — Representing Data

3 The time taken for 47 people to complete two crosswords is recorded. The axes on the left are for crossword A and the histogram on the right shows data for crossword B.

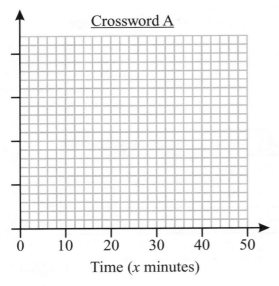

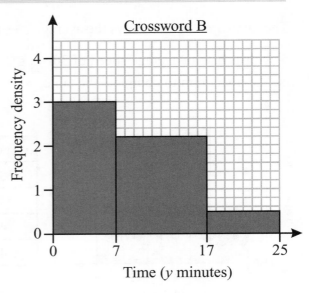

a) The data for crossword A is given in the table below.
Using the table, draw a histogram on the axes.

Time (x minutes)	$0 < x \le 5$	$5 < x \le 10$	$10 < x \le 20$	$20 < x \le 50$
Frequency	4	10	18	15

[5]

b) Estimate the number of people who completed crossword A in less than 15 minutes.

....

[2]

c) Find the modal class for crossword B. Explain your answer.

> The modal class has the highest frequency.

....

....

[2]

d) Is it appropriate to compare the times using the two histograms? Explain your answer.

....

....

[1]

[Total 10 marks]

Exam Practice Tip

There are a few important things to remember for histograms with unequal class widths (for Higher only):
1) <u>Frequency</u> is represented by the <u>area</u> of the bars instead of the height.
2) Frequency density goes on the <u>y-axis</u> and is found using: <u>frequency density = frequency ÷ class width</u>.

Score

19

The Shape of a Distribution

1 The histograms below show the salaries of employees (in thousands of £) in two companies.

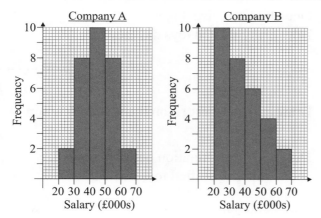

The median for one company is £45 000 and the median for the other is £36 250.

a) Identify the median of company A and the median of company B.

Company A median = ...

Company B median = ...

[1]

b) Compare the distributions of the salaries for the two companies in context.

....

....

[2]

c) Which one of the following statements is true for Company B? Circle your answer.

mean > median > mode   **mean = median = mode**   **mean < median < mode**

[1]

[Total 4 marks]

2 The stem and leaf diagram below shows the runs scored by two cricketers in 15 matches.

Cricketer A   Cricketer B

```
              9 0 0 │ 0 │ 5
3 | 4 = 43 runs   8 5 1 │ 1 │ 7 8      4 | 7 = 47 runs
              5 5 3 │ 2 │ 0 6 8
    no stem?      8 7 2 │ 3 │ 3 3 3 8 9  negative.
              3 1 0 │ 4 │ 2 3 6 7
```

a) Compare the distributions of the runs scored by the two cricketers in context.

....

....

[2]

b) Which cricketer generally scored more runs? Give a reason for your answer.

....

[1]

[Total 3 marks]

Score:

7

Section Three — Representing Data

Scatter Diagrams

1   The scatter diagram shows the shoe size and the number of stuffed toys owned by 10 children.

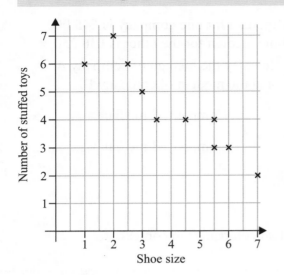

a)   One child had size 3 feet.
     How many stuffed toys did they own?

     ....

     [1]

b)   Draw a line of best fit on the scatter diagram.

     [1]

c)   Describe the correlation between shoe size
     and number of stuffed toys owned.

     ....

     [1]

[Total 3 marks]

2   Adult humans have a maximum of 32 teeth. A dentist takes a sample of 20 patients.
    She records each patient's age in years, x, and the number of teeth they have with no fillings, t.

Age, x (years)	30	40	25	31	20	35	10	46	54	60	25	40	50	60	50	45	50	15	55	42
Number of teeth without fillings, t	28	22	27	26	28	24	28	25	22	22	25	24	25	20	20	22	23	31	20	18

a)   Explain why it is appropriate to show this data on a scatter diagram.

     ....

     [1]

b)   Draw a scatter diagram for this data
     on the axes given.

     [2]

c)   Draw a line of best fit on
     your scatter diagram.

     [1]

d)   Describe and interpret the correlation
     between patient age and the number
     of teeth with no fillings.

     ....

     ....

     ....

     [2]

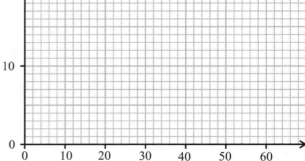

[Total 6 marks]

Score:

9

Time Series Graphs

1   A gardener records the temperature in her greenhouse every 2 hours over a 12-hour period.
    Her results are shown in the table below.

Time	09:00	11:00	13:00	15:00	17:00	19:00	21:00
Temperature (°C)	27	28	30	31.5	30.5	29	28

a)   Draw a time series graph to show her data.

[2]

b)   Comment on the trend of the data.

    ....

    ....

    ....

[1]

[Total 3 marks]

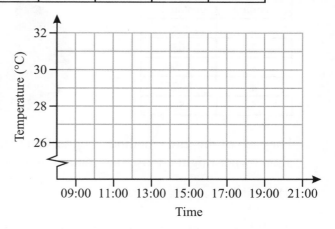

2   Elle writes down the value of her car in the first 8 months of 2018 in the table below.

Month	J	F	M	A	M	J	J	A
Value of car (£)	770	750	710	670	650	660	620	580

a)   Draw a time series graph to show her data. Add a trend line to your graph.

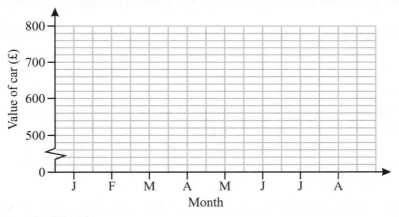

[3]

b)   Comment on the trend of the data.

    ....

[1]

c)   Use your trend line to predict the value of the car in September.

    ....

[1]

[Total 5 marks]

Score:

8

Section Three — Representing Data

Choosing How to Represent Data

1 A shop owner recorded the number of customers who made a purchase in the first 5 weeks after the shop opened. She uses the three methods below to represent the data with statistical software.

Method 1: Table

Week after opening	Number of customers
1	875
2	1050
3	1200
4	1375
5	1500

Method 2: Pie chart

Method 3: Time series graph

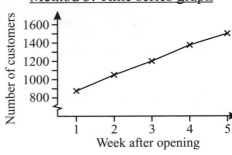

For each of the three methods, suggest one reason why the shop owner might choose that method to represent her data.

To get full marks, give a different reason for each method.

Method 1 ....

Method 2 ....

Method 3 ....

[Total 3 marks]

2 Mo has collected data about the distance walked to school by 100 students. He is planning how to represent and communicate his results.

a) (i) Explain why it would **not** be appropriate to represent Mo's data on a stem and leaf diagram.

....

[1]

(ii) Explain why it would be appropriate to represent Mo's data on a cumulative frequency diagram.

....

[1]

b) Mo considers using a histogram to present the data to a class of Year 7 students. Explain whether or not a histogram would be appropriate for his target audience.

....

....

[1]

[Total 3 marks]

Exam Practice Tip

When choosing how to represent data, think about the type of data you have. Some diagrams might only be appropriate for discrete/continuous data — and if you have lots of data values you might group the data. You should consider whether diagrams are useful to your hypothesis and appropriate for your audience.

Score

6

Misleading Diagrams

1 Jason drew the pictogram below, showing the type of lunch 20 students ate one lunchtime.

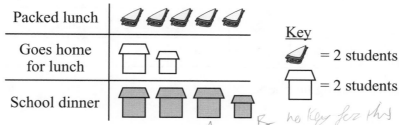

Identify **three** ways that Jason's diagram could be misleading.

....

....

....

[Total 3 marks]

2 A report on the levels of pollution caused by vehicles contains the graph below, which shows the number of flights per day from a particular airport over time.

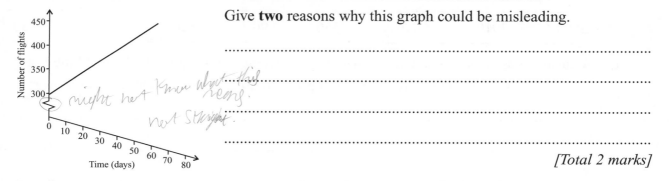

Give **two** reasons why this graph could be misleading.

....

....

....

....

[Total 2 marks]

3 A restaurant chain has three restaurants, A, B and C. The pie charts below show the same data for the proportion of profit by each of the restaurants.

Chart 1
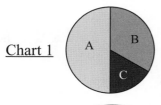

Chart 2
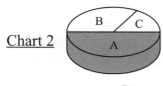

Chart 3
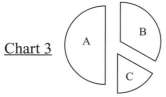

The owner of restaurant A wants to show that her restaurant makes the most profit.

Which pie chart might she choose to put in a presentation to emphasise her point? Explain your answer.

....

....

....

[Total 2 marks]

Score:

7

Section Three — Representing Data

Mean, Median and Mode

1   The mean of twelve numbers is 5 and the mode is 7. Ten of the numbers are shown in the table.

1	5	7	2	3	
6	7	9	8	2	

a)   Fill in the two missing numbers.

[3]

b)   Calculate the median of the twelve numbers.

....

[2]

[Total 5 marks]

2   A manufacturer tested the lifetimes (to the nearest 10 hours) of a type of LED light bulb so that he could confidently say how long they lasted. The results for eight such light bulbs are as follows:

3090	2010	2010	2550	90	2620	2800	2550

a)   A customer asks the manufacturer how long, on average, this type of LED light bulb lasts.

(i)   Which type of average would be appropriate to use? Give a reason for your answer.

....

....

....

[2]

(ii)   Calculate the average lifetime of a bulb, using your choice from part (i).

.... hours

[2]

b)   The manufacturer tests a ninth lightbulb and it lasts for 4000 hours.
Describe the effect that this would have on:

(i)   the mean lifetime,   (ii)   the median lifetime.

....

....

....

[2]

[Total 6 marks]

3 Ten cars undergo a test of their brakes. They each reach a speed of 70 km/h and then the driver performs an emergency stop. The times (in minutes) it took each car to stop are given below:

0.0365	0.0321	0.0364	0.0383	0.0301
0.0312	0.0363	0.0301	0.0357	0.0329

a) Using a suitable linear transformation, calculate the mean stopping time.

.... minutes

[3]

b) Give a reason why the mode would not be a suitable average to use in this case.

....

....

[1]

[Total 4 marks]

4 Jo is trying to decide which dress to buy: a blue one or a red one. She gives each dress a percentage score for looks, price and practicality. Each of these factors is weighted.

	Looks	Price	Practicality
Weight	0.3	0.5	0.2
Red	40%	30%	60%
Blue	45%	35%	20%

Using the scores and weights above, which dress should Jo buy? Show your working clearly.

....

[Total 3 marks]

5 A building society offers interest at a rate of 4% for the first year and 9% for the second year. A second building society offers a rate of 6.6% per year fixed over two years.

By calculating the geometric mean, determine which building society gives the best overall rate. Show all your working.

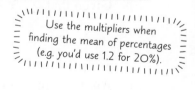

Use the multipliers when finding the mean of percentages (e.g. you'd use 1.2 for 20%).

....

[Total 3 marks]

Exam Practice Tip

The mean, median and mode are all useful for different things. As a rule of thumb, remember that the mode is good for qualitative data but not for continuous data, the median is good if there are outliers and the mean is good for large samples or if it's important to take account of all the values in the data set.

Score

21

Averages from Frequency Tables

1 A quality control department checked the number of nails in bags claiming to contain 100 nails.

Number of nails per bag	96	97	98	99	100	101	102	103	104
Number of bags	2	4	23	53	108	72	27	6	5

a) What is the modal number of nails in a bag?

....

[1]

b) What is the median number of nails in a bag?

....

[2]

c) Calculate the mean number of nails in a bag.

....

[2]

[Total 5 marks]

2 A group of university students was asked how many lectures they have each week.

Number of lectures, x	5	6	7	8	9	10	11	12	13	14	15	16
Frequency, f	12	10	5	24	18	8	5	20	12	3	2	p

a) (i) Given that the mode is 8, write down an inequality involving p.

....

[1]

(ii) Use the summary statistic $\sum f = 120$ to find the value of p.

$p =$ ....

[1]

b) Given that $\sum fx = 1128$, find the mean number of lectures.

....

[2]

c) Another student said that she has 30 lectures each week.
How would including this student in the analysis affect your answer to part b)?

....

[1]

[Total 5 marks]

Score:

10

Section Four — Analysing and Interpreting Data

Averages from Grouped Data

1 The times taken to get to work by employees of a stationery company are as follows:

Time (mins)	$0 \le t < 10$	$10 \le t < 20$	$20 \le t < 30$	$30 \le t < 40$	$40 \le t < 50$
Frequency	22	32	45	18	3

a) Calculate the estimated mean journey time, in minutes to 1 decimal place.

.... mins

[3]

b) Explain why your answer to part a) is an estimate.

....

[1]

c) Write down the modal class.

....

[1]

d) Use linear interpolation to calculate the median time, in minutes to 1 decimal place.

$27 + 32 + 45 + 18 + 3 = 120$ $120 \quad \frac{120}{2} = 60.5$

T	f	C.F.
	22	22
	32	54
$20 \le t < 30$	45	99

$\downarrow 10$

$60.5 - 54 = 6.5$

$\frac{6}{6}$

$\frac{6.5}{45} \times 10 = 1.44...$

$20 + 1.44... = 21.44... = 21.4$

$1.33...$

.... 21.4 mins

[3]

[Total 8 marks]

2 One of the competitions at a fête involved guessing the number of sweets in a jar. The guesses were recorded and put in the table below.

Guess	30-69	70-99	100-109	110-119	120-149	150-189
Frequency	2	15	24	24	18	8

a) In which group is the median number of sweets guessed?

....

[1]

b) Estimate the mean number of sweets guessed.

> Be careful with the classes — the data is discrete and the widths are unequal. E.g. for the first class, the midpoint is 50.

....

[3]

[Total 4 marks]

Score:

12

Higher

Measures of Spread

1   The following box shows the number of cars parked in a multistorey car park at midday on each day in October, rounded to the nearest 10. The values have been sorted into descending order.

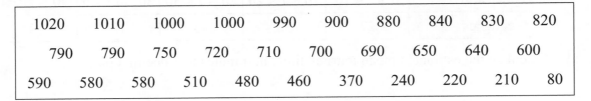

1020	1010	1000	1000	990	900	880	840	830	820
790	790	750	720	710	700	690	650	640	600
590	580	580	510	480	460	370	240	220	210	80

For the data given above, find:

a)   the upper quartile,

....

[1]

b)   the lower quartile,

....

[1]

c)   the interquartile range.

....

[1]

[Total 3 marks]

2   The weights of 12 mangos are recorded below.

| 245 g | 247 g | 233 g | 231 g | 258 g | 232 g |
| 242 g | 245 g | 250 g | 246 g | 239 g | 245 g |

a)   What is the range of the weights?

.... g

[1]

b)   Find the interquartile range of the data.

.... g

[2]

c)   The weights of a different 12 mangos have a lower quartile of 240 g and an upper quartile of 250 g. Compare and interpret the spread of the two sets of weights.

....

....

....

[2]

[Total 5 marks]

Section Four — Analysing and Interpreting Data

3 The table gives information on the birth weights of a sample of babies at two maternity hospitals.

	Lowest value	Lower quartile	Upper quartile	Highest value
Dr. Smith & Partners	1.0 kg	2.1 kg	3.7 kg	5.2 kg
Happy Tot Hospital	1.5 kg	2.4 kg	3.4 kg	5.4 kg

a) Use this information to compare the dispersion of the birth weights at Dr. Smith & Partners with the dispersion of the birth weights at the Happy Tot Hospital. Interpret your comparisons.

....

....

....

....

[4]

b) There were 23 babies in the sample from Dr. Smith & Partners.
How many babies had a birth weight of less than or equal to 2.1 kg?

....

[2]

[Total 6 marks]

4 Ellen measures the heights of a sample of 140 sunflowers.
She finds that they have a range of 120 cm and an interdecile range of 54 cm.

a) Determine how many sunflowers are not included when Ellen calculates the interdecile range.

....

[1]

b) Give one reason why the range is so much larger than the interdecile range.

....

....

[1]

c) Ellen says, "The interdecile range can never be larger than the range."
Is she correct? Justify your answer.

....

....

[1]

[Total 3 marks]

Score:

17

Higher

Section Four — Analysing and Interpreting Data

Measures of Spread — Grouped Data

1   In a survey, 120 people were asked how long, on average, they spend reading a particular Sunday newspaper. The cumulative frequency graph below shows the results.

a)   Estimate the value of the 35th percentile.

....

[1]

b)   Use the graph to estimate the interquartile range of the time spent reading the newspaper.

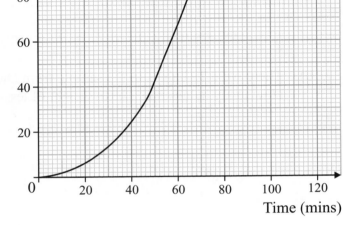

....

[2]

c)   Estimate the P_{60} to P_{80} interpercentile range for the data.

....

[2]

d)   The same group of people were asked how long they spend reading the television guide that comes with the newspaper. Here is some information to summarise their responses.

Median	20 minutes
P_{60} to P_{80} interpercentile range	15 minutes

Make two comparisons between the times spent reading the newspaper and the television guide. You should interpret your comparisons.

....

....

....

....

[3]

[Total 8 marks]

Higher

Section Four — Analysing and Interpreting Data

Score: ☐

8

Standard Deviation

1   For a set of 12 data values, $\sum x^2 = 3840$ and $\sum x = 208.8$.
    Use this information to calculate the standard deviation, σ, to 2 decimal places.

$$sd = \sqrt{\frac{\sum x^2}{n} - \left(\frac{\sum x}{n}\right)^2} \qquad \sqrt{\frac{3840}{12} - \left(\frac{208.8}{12}\right)^2}$$

$\sigma = \underline{\quad 4.15 \quad}$

$320 - 302.76$

[Total 2 marks]

$= 17.24$

$\sqrt{17.24} = 4.152107898.$

2   A man weighed himself on five different makes of bathroom scales.
    The results, x kilograms, are shown below.

| 85.8 | 85.9 | 86.0 | 85.7 | 85.9 |

a)   Calculate the mean weight, $\overline{x}$.

.... kg

[1]

b)   Calculate $\sum (x - \overline{x})^2$.

....

[2]

c)   Hence find the standard deviation of the weights. Give your answer to 3 significant figures.

.... kg

[1]

[Total 4 marks]

3   Consider the numbers 1-10 inclusive.

a)   Calculate the standard deviation of this set of values to 3 significant figures.

....

[2]

b)   Without any further calculation, write down the standard deviation of the numbers
    95-104 inclusive and give a brief explanation of why you know your answer is correct.

....

....

[1]

[Total 3 marks]

Exam Practice Tip

You'll be given the formulas for the standard deviation (σ) on your formula sheet, so don't worry too much about learning them. Do make sure you know what the parts of the formulas mean and how to use them. It's also important to be clear on what σ represents — it's the spread of the data <u>about the mean</u>.

Score

9

Standard Deviation from Frequency Tables

1 25 holidaymakers out crab-fishing were asked how many crabs they had caught in the last hour. The results are shown in the table below.

Number of crabs, x	0	1	2	3	4	5	6
Number of holidaymakers, f	3	2	5	6	6	2	1

a) Calculate the standard deviation of this data to 2 s.f., given that $\sum fx = 70$ and $\sum fx^2 = 258$.

....

[2]

b) The standard deviation for another group of holidaymakers was calculated and found to be 0.5. The mean number of crabs for this group was 3.1. Compare the distribution of crabs caught by the two groups of holidaymakers.

....

....

....

....

[3]

[Total 5 marks]

2 The table on the right shows the times, in seconds, taken by a group of 30 Year 11s to run 100 metres in an athletics lesson.

Time, t (seconds)	Frequency, f
$0 < t \le 15$	1
$15 < t \le 20$	8
$20 < t \le 25$	12
$25 < t \le 30$	8
$30 < t \le 35$	1
Total	30

a) Show that an estimate for the standard deviation for the times is 4.9 seconds, to 1 decimal place. You may use the statistic $\sum ft^2 = 15\,687.5$.

[2]

b) Explain why the answer to part a) is an estimate.

....

....

[1]

[Total 3 marks]

Exam Practice Tip

Sadly, you <u>do</u> need to learn the formulas for the standard deviation from frequency tables — but they're not all that different from the ones you're given in the exam. Replace all the n's with Σf's and stick an f in the numerator of all the fractions (in the right places, of course). That's all there is to it.

Score

8

Box Plots

1   Below is a list of the numbers of emails received by 23 office workers in one week.

0	8	10	11	12	12	15	17	24	24	25	26
28	32	32	34	37	38	50	55	67	74	76	

On the grid below, draw a box plot to represent this data.

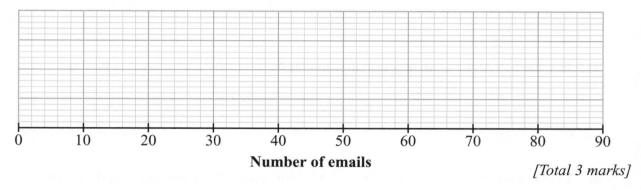

Number of emails

[Total 3 marks]

2   The following box plots summarise the GCSE French results for students of two schools — Abbeyknock and Blakeney.

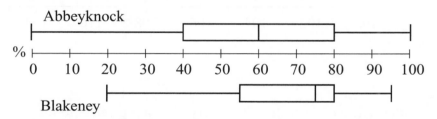

a)   Use the box plot to identify the average result for the students of Abbeyknock.

.... %

[1]

b)   Calculate the interquartile range of the results for the students of Blakeney.

.... %

[2]

c)   Discuss how the two schools' results compare with one another.

....

....

....

....

[4]

[Total 7 marks]

Score:

10

Section Four — Analysing and Interpreting Data

Outliers

1 The weights of 12 eggs are recorded and a box plot drawn to display the data.

102 g	110 g	105 g	102 g	114 g	103 g
103 g	101 g	106 g	101 g	104 g	105 g

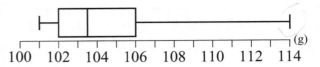

a) Use inspection to identify a possible outlier.

114 ✓

....

[1]

b) Use the box plot and an appropriate calculation to verify your answer to part a).

UQ = 106.

106 + (1.5 × (106 − 102) = 112.

114 > 112 so is outlier.

[3]

c) On the grid below, draw a new box plot for this data, taking into account the outlier.

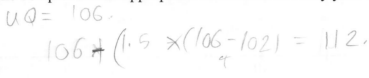

(g)

[1]

[Total 5 marks]

2 The number of cherries, *c*, on each of 20 cherry trees are given below.

| 25 | 26 | 58 | 30 | 35 | 27 | 40 | 37 | 24 | 34 | 33 | 27 | 45 | 42 | 29 | 38 | 33 | 31 | 24 | 48 |

a) Find the mean number of cherries.

....

[2]

b) Given that $\sum (c - \bar{c})^2 = 1512.2$, calculate the standard deviation of these values to 2 d.p.

....

[1]

c) Hence find by calculation any outliers in the data.

....

[2]

[Total 5 marks]

Score

10

Higher

Section Four — Analysing and Interpreting Data

Skewness of Data

1   The box plots of two distributions have been drawn below.

Histograms and skew are covered in Section Three.

For each one: (i) state the type of skew shown,
              (ii) sketch the shape of a possible histogram of the distribution on the axes given.

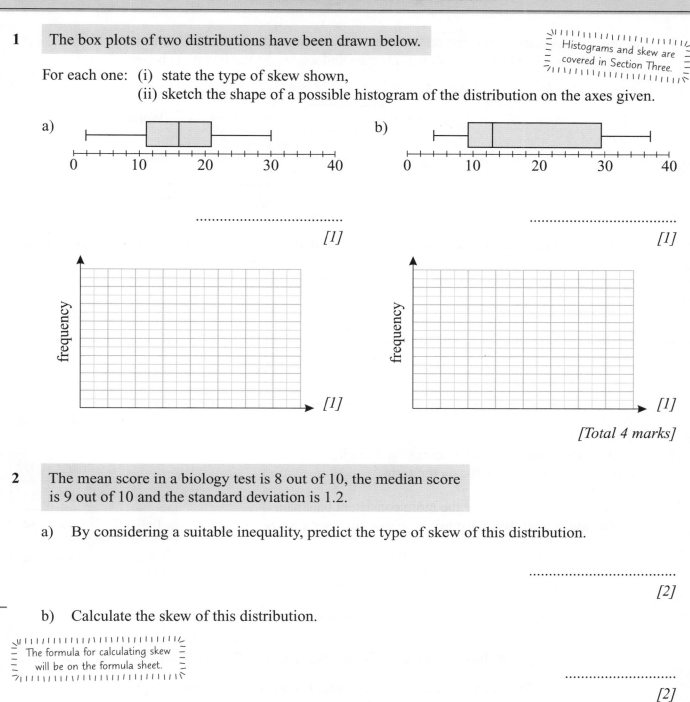

a)

....
[1]

b)

....
[1]

frequency

[1]

frequency

[1]

[Total 4 marks]

2   The mean score in a biology test is 8 out of 10, the median score
    is 9 out of 10 and the standard deviation is 1.2.

a)   By considering a suitable inequality, predict the type of skew of this distribution.

....
[2]

b)   Calculate the skew of this distribution.

The formula for calculating skew will be on the formula sheet.

....
[2]

c)   Interpret the skew in context.

....

....

[1]

[Total 5 marks]

Higher

Exam Practice Tip

It's easy to get mixed up when spotting skew. For positive skew, data below the median is more compact so the median bar is to the left of the box and the peak of a histogram is to the left of the graph. This means most of the data is relatively low (not high, as the word 'positive' might imply).

Score

9

Comparing Data Sets

1   A survey asks respondents the distance they travel commuting between home and work in a day. The results are shown for men and women in the box plots below.

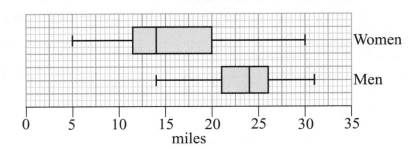

Use this information to compare the distances travelled by the men and by the women in the survey.

....

....

....

....

....

[Total 4 marks]

2   A summary of two batsmen's scores for a cricket season is shown in the table on the right.

	A	B
Mean	57	51
Median	48	54
Interquartile range	24	26

a)   Batsman A claims to be the more consistent batsman. Do you agree? You must give a reason for your answer.

....

....

....

[2]

b)   A cricket magazine has an article on the two players. The following statement is in the article:

"Batsman A is generally the better batsman — his score is higher on average and this is linked to his more consistent scores."

Do you think this is a valid statement? Give a reason for your answer.

....

....

[2]

[Total 4 marks]

Exam Practice Tip

There are three things you need to think about when comparing data sets — the average value (the median or the mean), the spread of the data (a range or the standard deviation) and the skew (which you might have to read off the box plot or calculate). Then don't forget to interpret them all in context.

Score

8

Section Four — Analysing and Interpreting Data

Standardised Scores

1 At a hospital fun day, a group of doctors and nurses sit on a mechanical rodeo bull. The mean and standard deviation of the times that they remain on the bull are shown in the table below.

	Mean (μ)	Standard Deviation (σ)
Nurses	30 s	4.6 s
Doctors	25 s	6.7 s

The formula won't be given so you'll have to learn it:

$$\text{standardised score} = \frac{value - \mu}{\sigma}$$

a) What is the standardised value (to 3 s.f.) for a nurse who remained on the bull for 32 seconds?

....

[2]

b) The standardised value for a doctor was calculated to be 0.343 (3 s.f.). What was the actual length of time that the doctor remained on the bull, to 3 significant figures?

.... seconds

[2]

[Total 4 marks]

2 20 dancers took part in a competition involving a compulsory and a freestyle dance. For each dance, a maximum score of 50 was possible. The scores awarded to two of the competitors, Nathan and Zac, and the mean and standard deviation overall for each dance are shown below.

	Nathan's Scores	Zac's Scores	Mean	Standard Deviation
Compulsory	43	40	37.25	5.07
Freestyle	41	44	41.7	3.2

a) (i) Using the information above, calculate Zac's standardised compulsory and freestyle scores. Add these scores together to find his total score to 3 significant figures.

....

[3]

(ii) Who gave the better overall performance, Nathan or Zac? Explain your answer.

....

[3]

b) Another competitor, Chin-Sun, had a standardised score of 0.15 for the compulsory dance. Calculate her original score to the nearest whole number.

....

[2]

[Total 8 marks]

Score:

12

Summary Statistics — Index Numbers

1 The escalating price of a luxury food hamper is shown in the table below.

Year	2015	2016	2017	2018
Price (£)	420	425	430	450

a) Using 2015 as the base year, calculate the index number for 2018 to 1 decimal place.

£107.1 ✓

[2]

b) The table on the right shows information about the annual average consumer price index (CPI) for 2015, 2016 and 2017.

Year	2015	2016	2017
CPI	100	100.7	102.7

Source: adapted from data from the Office for National Statistics

Describe how the increase in the price of the food hamper compares with the CPI between 2015 and 2016 **and** between 2015 and 2017.

100.7   102.7   shew nexflen is hex?

betwee 2015-2016 the price rose by 0.7 and between 2015-2017 it rose by 2.7 showing that it is increasing and exponentially as if the rate had stayed the same it would have been by 1.4 instead. Lots of things I don't see to understand due to it being Edexcel.

[5]

[Total 7 marks]

---

2 A smoothie is made using milk, bananas and strawberries.
The amount spent on the ingredients in 2017 and 2018 is shown in the table below.

	2017	2018	Weight
Milk	£1.00	£1.20	58
Bananas	44p	52p	25
Strawberries	30p	38p	17

Using 2017 as the base year, calculate the weighted index number for 2018.
Give your answer correct to 4 significant figures.

Milk - 1.20/1.00 × 100 = 120
Bananas   52/44 × 100 = 118.1818182
Strawberries   38/30 × 100 = 126.6666667
= 364.848489
× 100 ÷ 3 = 12,161.6616

*58 × 120 = *
25 = 118... 696455
× 17 = 2153.3
= 12967878

This method

58 × 120 = 6960
= 12967878
÷ 58+25 + 17
= 58+26 + 17
= 120.6787879
= 120.7

12,160 ✗

[Total 4 marks]

Section Four — Analysing and Interpreting Data

3 A company uses two different types of steel to make an aircraft part. Each part requires 6 units of steel A and 4 units of steel B. In 2017, the price per unit of each type of steel was the same.

Year	2017	2018	Weight
Steel A	£275.00	£280.00	3
Steel B	£275.00	£305.00	

a) Complete the table.

[1]

b) Using 2017 as the base year, what is the weighted index number for 2018 (to 1 d.p.)?

....
[4]

c) By what percentage did the price of the steel increase between 2017 and 2018?

.... %
[1]

[Total 6 marks]

4 The table below shows the average weekly earnings for the United Kingdom from 2014 to 2017.

Year	2014	2015	2016	2017
Earnings (£)	471	483	495	506

Source: adapted from data from the Office for National Statistics

a) Calculate the chain base index numbers for 2015, 2016 and 2017 (to 2 d.p.).

2015: ....   2016: ....   2017: ....

[3]

b) Explain what each of these chain base index numbers shows.

....

....

....

[3]

[Total 6 marks]

Higher

Exam Practice Tip

Don't be put off if an index number that you're not expecting comes up. RPI, CPI and GDP are some real-life examples, but there's nothing stopping the examiners throwing in some that aren't listed here. The main thing is they work the same way — just make sure you know whether it's normal, weighted or chain based.

Score

23

Summary Statistics — Rates of Change

1 Some statistics about the towns of Wentwell and Bourneland for the year 2017 are presented in the table below.

Town	Population	Number of births	Crude birth rate (1 d.p.)
Wentwell	28 600	432	
Bourneland	15 000		21.4

a) Complete the table.

[3]

b) How many births were there in Wentwell per **hundred** of population?

....

[1]

[Total 4 marks]

2 The number of deaths in two towns, Mudgrave and Ollington, last year are shown in the table.

Age Group	Mudgrave		Ollington	
	Population	Number of deaths	Population	Number of deaths
<40	57 000	120	80 000	100
40-60	30 000	320	49 000	500
>60	44 000	5260	86 000	8050

a) Calculate the crude death rates for Mudgrave and Ollington to 1 decimal place.

A crude rate of change formula will be given to you in the exam.

Mudgrave .... Ollington ....

[3]

b) Which town seems to have the healthier population?

....

[1]

c) Explain why it may be better to use standardised death rates to compare the two towns.

....

....

....

[2]

[Total 6 marks]

Higher

3 The age distribution for the towns Hadham and Lostham are given in the table below.

a) Which town is likely to have a higher crude birth rate? Give a reason for your answer.

....

....

[1]

Age Group	Hadham %	Lostham %
0 - 15	12	3
16 - 30	33	19
31 - 45	37	25
46 - 60	15	33
over 60	3	20

b) Is the standardised birth rate for Hadham likely to be higher or lower than its crude birth rate? Give a reason for your answer.

....

....

[1]

[Total 2 marks]

4 The table below shows information about the ages of people and the number of deaths in the United Kingdom in 2011.

Age Group	Population (5 s.f.)	Standard population	Number of deaths
0 - 14	11 100 000		4213
15 - 64	41 706 000		78 038
65 or older	10 376 000		402 116
Total	63 182 000	1000	

Source: adapted from data from the Office for National Statistics

a) Work out the crude death rate of the United Kingdom in 2011 to 3 significant figures.

....

[2]

b) Calculate the standard population of the United Kingdom and write your answers in the table.

[3]

c) Show that the standardised death rate for the United Kingdom using this standard population is 1.9 deaths per thousand of population (to 1 decimal place).

[3]

[Total 8 marks]

Score:

20

Section Four — Analysing and Interpreting Data

Estimating Population Characteristics

1 Samar has a large number of slugs in her garden. She measures a sample of ten slugs, and records the following lengths (in cm).

| 12 | 14 | 12.5 | 11.5 | 13.5 | 13 | 12 | 10 | 11 | 13 |

a) Use Samar's measurements to estimate the mean length of all the slugs in her garden.

.... cm

[2]

b) Give one reason why this result might be unreliable.

....

....

[1]

c) Samar tells her friends that the answer to part a) is the average length of all the slugs in the UK. Give one reason why she is wrong to do this.

....

....

[1]

[Total 4 marks]

2 A farmer has 30 henhouses, each housing the same number of hens. He collected and counted the eggs from six of these houses on the same day. The results are shown below.

| 37 | 43 | 35 | 45 | 42 | 38 |

a) How many eggs, on average, does each of these henhouses yield?

....

[1]

b) How many eggs would the farmer expect to get altogether each day?

....

[2]

c) By considering the quartiles of the farmer's data, estimate how many of the henhouses will produce 43 or more eggs each day.

....

[2]

[Total 5 marks]

Score:

9

Estimating Population Sizes

1 State whether the Petersen capture recapture method would be suitable for estimating each of the following. Give a reason for your choice.

a) The number of people on a cruise ship.

....

....

[1]

b) The number of trees in a forest.

....

....

[1]

[Total 2 marks]

2 An environmental health inspector visited a food storage warehouse one morning. She caught ten mice and tagged each of them. She returned that afternoon and caught eight mice, two of which had tags on.

a) Estimate how many mice there are in the warehouse.

....

[2]

b) Write down one assumption you have made about the mouse population.

....

....

[1]

[Total 3 marks]

3 A group wants to find out how many deer live in a wood. One afternoon, the group harmlessly marks 3 deer, then safely releases them. Ten months later, the group returns to the wood and finds 20 deer. Since 1 of these is marked, they conclude that there are 60 deer in the wood.

Do you think this is an accurate conclusion? Justify your answer. Do **not** check the group's working.

....

....

....

[Total 2 marks]

Exam Practice Tip

Knowing the formula for Petersen's capture recapture method is only half the battle — it's just as important to know when to use it. The population needs to be constant (i.e. no one enters or leaves), both samples have to be representative, the tagged subjects need to mix back in and the tagging mustn't affect the subjects.

Score

7

Section Four — Analysing and Interpreting Data

Interpreting Scatter Diagrams

1   A drilling ship measures the temperature, $t\,°C$, at various depths, d km, below the
     seabed as it drills into the Earth's crust. The table below shows these measurements.

d (km)	1.2	1.5	2.1	2.3	3.1	3.3	3.5	3.8
t (°C)	18	24	30	36	40	46	46	48

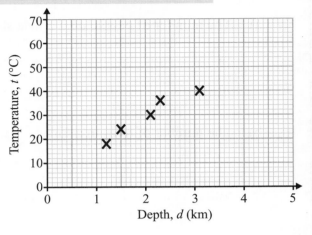

a)   Plot the last three points in the table
     on the scatter diagram on the right.

                                                              [1]

b)   Use the diagram to describe and
     interpret the correlation between
     temperature and depth.

     ....

     ....
                                                                                                    [2]

c)   (i)   The mean depth of the measurements in the table is 2.6 km.
           Find the mean temperature.

                                                              .... °C
                                                                    [2]

     (ii) Hence draw a line of best fit on the graph and label it L.

                                                                    [1]

d)   Use your line of best fit to estimate:

     (i)   the temperature at a depth of 2 km below the seabed,

                                                              .... °C
                                                                    [1]

     (ii) the temperature on the seabed. Comment on the reliability of your answer.

           ....

           ....
                                                                                                    [2]

e)   The captain of the ship uses the regression line $t = -6 + 16d$ to plan how deep to drill.

     (i)   Draw the captain's regression line on the graph above and label it K.

                                                                                                    [2]

     (ii) Interpret the value of the gradient of the captain's regression line.

           ....

           ....
                                                                                                    [2]

                                                                          [Total 13 marks]

Higher

2 A weather forecaster collects data from 10 different meteorological stations. The scatter diagram shows the average weekly temperature, T °C, and the total weekly rainfall, R mm, for nine of these stations for one week.

a) The tenth station recorded 17 mm of rainfall and a temperature of 6 °C. Use this information to complete the scatter diagram.

[1]

b) (i) The weather forecaster says that the greater the amount of rainfall, the lower the temperature. Explain with a statistical reason whether the diagram supports this claim.

....

....

....

[2]

(ii) The forecaster then says that an increased amount of rainfall causes cooler temperatures. Comment on whether the data justifies the forecaster's conclusion.

....

....

[1]

c) The regression line passes through the points (19, 9) and (11, 12). Determine the equation of the regression line in the form $T = a + bR$.

....

[2]

d) An eleventh weather station records a total weekly rainfall of 18 mm. Use the **equation** of the regression line to estimate the average weekly temperature at this station to 1 d.p.

.... °C

[2]

e) Explain whether it would be appropriate to use this regression line to predict the average weekly temperature at a weather station that recorded 17 mm of rain.

....

....

[1]

[Total 9 marks]

Exam Practice Tip

Correlation does not imply causation — a phrase that every statistician should hold dear. Remember that just because two variables both change, it doesn't mean that a change in one causes a change in the other. There could be other factors which are the cause for changes in both variables, or it might be a coincidence.

Score

22

Section Five — Analysing and Interpreting Diagrams

Spearman's Rank Correlation Coefficient

1   A sports club goes out each weekend to try different sports. One weekend they went to a karting circuit and the next they went to a dry ski slope. Each member of the club noted their times in the two activities. These are recorded on the right.

	Karting time (sec)	Skiing time (sec)
Agneta	56	65
Bashshar	62	62
Chaz	51	60
Dalia	64	58
Eric	53	59

The club's organiser calculates Spearman's rank correlation coefficient for the karting times and the skiing times. He obtains a value of −0.2.

a)   State the type and strength of the correlation that this value represents.

her Correlation.

[1]

b)   Interpret the club organiser's value in context.

The club member's time Karting had no effect on how long they skied for.

[1]

[Total 2 marks]

2   Eight singers in a competition perform a single song. Two judges award a mark out of 10 to each singer, with higher marks given for better performances.

a)   Work out Spearman's rank correlation coefficient for the judges' scores to 2 decimal places.

The S.R.C.C. formula will be on your formula sheet.

0.43

[4]

Singer	A	B	C	D	E	F	G	H
Judge 1	8	6	10	9	5	7	4	3
Judge 2	6	7	9	10	5	3	4	8
Rank J1	6	4	8	7	3	5	2	1
Rank J2	4	5	7	8	3	1	2	6
d	2	-1	-1	-1	0	4	0	-5
d²	4	+1	1	+1	0	16	0	+25

b)   Use your answer to part a) to determine how much agreement there is between the two judges.

Shows a weak positive correlation, there is some agreement between the judges

[2]

c)   A third judge has scored the same singers. Spearman's rank correlation coefficient for Judge 2 and Judge 3 is 1.0 exactly. Based on this information alone, what can be said about Judge 3's opinion of Singer F's performance?

The Judges must have agreed completely so Judge 3 ranked singer F as a 3 too.

[1]

[Total 7 marks]

Score:

9

Interpreting Correlation Coefficients

1 For each of the scatter diagrams below, circle one value to show a possible Pearson's product moment correlation coefficient and one value to show a possible Spearman's rank correlation coefficient.

a)

Pearson's product moment correlation coefficient:

−1   −0.5   0   0.5   ⟨1⟩

Spearman's rank correlation coefficient:

−1   −0.5   0   0.5   ⟨1⟩

[2]

b)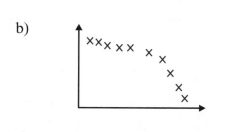

Pearson's product moment correlation coefficient:

−1   ⟨−0.5⟩   0   0.5   1

Spearman's rank correlation coefficient:

⟨−1⟩   −0.5   0   0.5   1

[2]

[Total 4 marks]

2 Two friends at a cake tasting were asked to award marks out of ten for eight different cakes. They find that Pearson's product moment correlation coefficient for their sets of scores is 0.5.

a) Interpret this value in context.

....

....

[1]

b) (i) The scatter diagram on the right shows the relationship between the two friends' scores. Use the diagram to write down a possible value for Spearman's rank correlation coefficient for their sets of scores.

....

[1]

(ii) Give a reason for your answer to part (i).

....

....

[2]

[Total 4 marks]

Exam Practice Tip

Pearson's P.M.C.C. and Spearman's R.C.C. both quantify association between variables, but it's important to remember how they differ. Pearson's can only detect a <u>linear</u> correlation (how close points are to a straight line) but Spearman's can detect any increasing or decreasing association, even if it's non-linear.

Score

8

Section Five — Analysing and Interpreting Diagrams

Time Series

1   The total number of guests staying at a hotel in each quarter of the year is recorded in the table below (rounded to the nearest 10). Most of the four-point moving averages have been calculated.

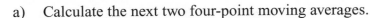

Year	2014				2015				2016				2017			
Quarter	1	2	3	4	1	2	3	4	1	2	3	4	1	2	3	4
Number of guests	800	850	900	700	790	830	890	700	780	830	870	690	770	820	860	680
Four-point moving average		812.5	810	805	802.5	802.5	800	800	795	792.5	790	787.5				

a)   Calculate the next two four-point moving averages.

....

[3]

b)   The number of guests staying each quarter and the first five moving averages have been plotted on the graph on the right. Finish plotting the averages and draw a trend line.

[3]

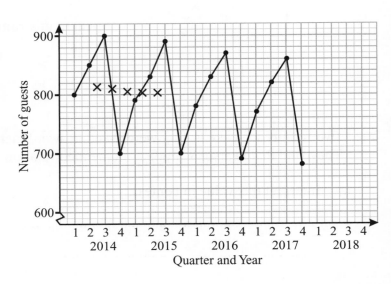

c)   Which quarter had the smallest number of guests every year?

....

[1]

d)   Describe and interpret the trend in the number of guests from 2014 to 2017.

....

....

[2]

e)   Compare and interpret the seasonal variation in the number of guests for the four quarters.

....

....

[2]

f)   Explain whether you can use this time series to determine how many guests visited in 2012.

....

....

[2]

[Total 13 marks]

2 The table below shows the termly fuel bills paid by a secondary school over four years.

Year	2015	2015	2015	2016	2016	2016	2017	2017	2017	2018	2018	2018
Term	1	2	3	1	2	3	1	2	3	1	2	3
Cost of Fuel (£000)	19.2	15.4	14.3	19.8	15.7	14.3	20.4	15.7	14.6	21.0	16.3	14.9
3-point moving average		16.3	16.5	16.6	16.6	16.8	16.8	16.9	17.1	17.3		

a) Calculate the missing 3-point moving average.

....

[2]

b) The data for the school's fuel bills each term from 2015 to 2018 has been plotted on the time series graph below. Plot your answer from part a) and draw a trend line for the time series.

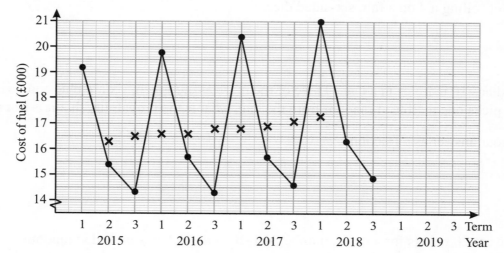

[2]

c) Calculate the seasonal effect for Term 2 of 2016.

....

[1]

d) Calculate the average seasonal effect for Term 2.

....

[2]

e) Use the trend line and your answer to part d) to estimate the cost of fuel in Term 2 of 2019.

£ ....

[2]

f) Explain why 3-point moving averages have been chosen in this case.

....

[1]

[Total 10 marks]

Score:

23

Section Five — Analysing and Interpreting Diagrams

Higher

Probability

1 On the probability scale below, mark with a cross the probabilities of events a)-c).

Make sure you label each event.

```
├──────────────────┼──────────────────┤
0                  0.5                 1
```

a) Rolling an odd number on a fair, six-sided dice.

[1]

b) Rolling a number less than 7 on a fair, six-sided dice.

[1]

c) **Not** rolling a 4 on a fair, six-sided dice.

[1]

[Total 3 marks]

2 David has 10 marbles in a bag. Three of the marbles are green, six are blue and one is silver. If he picks one marble at random from the bag, what is the probability that it is **not** silver?

Give your answer as a fraction.

....

[Total 1 mark]

3 There are 20 tickets for a raffle, numbered 1-20. One ticket is picked at random.

a) What is the probability of picking ticket 16?
Give your answer as a percentage.

....

[1]

b) What is the probability that the selected ticket shows a prime number?
Give your answer as a decimal.

> Remember, a prime number has
> only two factors — itself and 1.

....

[3]

[Total 4 marks]

4 The pupils in a year group are divided into four forms: A, B, C and D.

$\frac{3}{10}$ of the pupils are in form A, $\frac{1}{5}$ are in B and $\frac{3}{20}$ are in C. What is the probability that a randomly selected pupil is in form D? Give your answer as a fraction in its simplest form.

....

[Total 2 marks]

Score:

10

Relative Frequency and Risk

1 Sam has a hexagonal spinner with sections numbered from 1 to 6.
To investigate whether or not the spinner is fair, he spins it 50 times
and records how often the spinner lands on each number.

Number on spinner	1	2	3	4	5	6
Frequency	14	5	7	8	6	10

a) Calculate the relative frequency of spinning a '1'.

0.28

[1]

b) Sam says that the spinner is **not** fair because it is biased to land on '1'.
Using your answer to part a), explain why Sam may be right that the spinner is biased.

*Fair spinner = 1/6 = 0.166... 0.28 is larger than this
suggesting bias.*

[2]

[Total 3 marks]

2 Amani works at a nature reserve. Over the summer, she records how often she sees a
natterjack toad. She sees a natterjack toad on 16 days and doesn't see one on 80 days.

Find the relative frequency of Amani seeing a natterjack toad.

$\frac{16}{96}$ = 0.166...

*$\frac{16}{96}$
0.167*

[Total 2 marks]

3 In a school, 48 out of the 100 boys in Year 11 have broken a bone during their life.

a) Calculate the absolute risk that a randomly selected boy from Year 11 will have broken a bone.

0.48

[1]

b) Nine out of the 150 girls in Year 11 have broken a bone during their life.
Find the relative risk of having broken a bone for Year 11 boys compared to
Year 11 girls and interpret your answer in context.

*9/150 = 3/50 = 0.06
0.48 ÷ 0.06 = 8*

*boys are ×8 more likely to have broken a bone than
girls.*

[3]

[Total 4 marks]

Exam Practice Tip	**Score**
Remember — absolute risk is the same as relative frequency, so use the same method to work it out. Relative risk is how many times more (or less) likely one event is to happen than another. To calculate the relative risk, you need to divide the absolute risk for the first event by the absolute risk for the second event.	**9**

Expected and Actual Frequencies

1   A factory produces chocolate penguins which have a 5% probability of being misshapen, and boxes of chocolate frogs which have a 10% probability of failing a quality check.

a)   The factory produces 280 chocolate penguins in an hour. Find the expected number of misshapen penguins that will be produced in this hour.

....
[1]

b)   120 boxes of frogs are checked for quality each day.
How many boxes would you expect to pass the quality check each day?

....
[2]

[Total 3 marks]

2   Lucy's quiz team regularly takes part in school quizzes. For any quiz they enter, there are three possible outcomes — they finish first, finish second, or finish third or worse. She predicts that the outcomes have probabilities 0.7, 0.2 and 0.1 respectively. This month, the team will enter 10 quizzes.

a)   Complete this table showing the expected frequencies of each outcome:

Outcome	First	Second	Third or worse
Expected Frequency	....	....	....

[2]

b)   The table below shows the outcomes of the quizzes. Draw a graph comparing the expected frequencies with the actual frequencies.

Quiz	1	2	3	4	5
Outcome	1st	1st	1st	2nd	1st

Quiz	6	7	8	9	10
Outcome	1st	1st	1st	1st	1st

[2]

c)   How could Lucy test her predictions more accurately?

....

....

[1]

[Total 5 marks]

Score: _____

8

Section Six — Probability

Sample Space Diagrams

1 The fair spinner on the right is spun, and a standard fair dice is rolled. The scores from the spinner and the dice are added together.

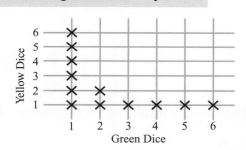

a) Draw a sample space diagram to show all the possible outcomes of the total score.

[2]

b) Use your sample space diagram to find the probability of getting a total of 9 or more.

....

[2]

[Total 4 marks]

2 Rahim has started to draw a Cartesian grid to work out the possible outcomes of throwing two standard dice, one green and one yellow.

a) Complete the grid to show all possible outcomes.

[1]

b) Find the probability of:
   (i) getting two odd numbers,

....

[1]

   (ii) getting a total of less than 8,

....

[2]

   (iii) getting two numbers whose difference is 3.

....

[2]

[Total 6 marks]

Score:

10

Section Six — Probability

Venn Diagrams and Two-Way Tables

1 A hot dog stand offers both ketchup and mustard as sauces for their hot dogs. One day the hot dog seller records the choices of a large number of customers. He finds that, of the people who bought a hot dog, a total of 14% had ketchup, a total of 8% had mustard and 2% had both.

a) Complete the Venn diagram to show this information.

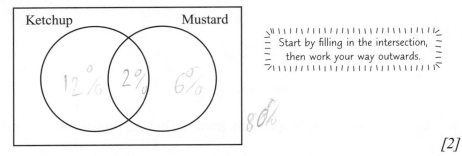

Start by filling in the intersection, then work your way outwards.

[2]

b) Find the probability, as a fraction, that a customer had either sauce on their hot dog.

20/100 / 20% ✓

[1]

c) The following day, 275 customers buy a hot dog. Using the previous day's results, how many customers would the hot dog seller expect to have just ketchup?

$275 \times \frac{12}{100} = 33$

33 ✓

[2]

[Total 5 marks]

2 A two-way table showing the results of a traffic survey is given below.

a) Complete the table.

	Red	Blue	Green	White	Total
Car	12	12	....	3	32
Lorry	2	1	0	11	....
Motorbike	....	2	0	1	4
Total	....	....	....	....	....

[3]

b) A vehicle is selected at random from the survey. Find the probability that the vehicle is:
   (i) a green motorbike,

[1]

   (ii) blue.

[1]

[Total 5 marks]

3 A pizza delivery company employs 40 people to deliver pizzas to customers.
Employees each use one of three methods of transport.
Some employees deliver by car, others use a moped, and the remainder deliver on foot.

30% of all employees deliver on foot.
Of the female employees, $\frac{1}{3}$ use a car. Of those employees delivering on foot, $\frac{1}{3}$ are male.

a) Complete the table to show all the information.

	Car	Moped	Foot	Total
Male	....	....	....	....
Female	....	....	....	15
Total	20	....	....	40

[3]

b) The manager selects a delivery person at random. Find the probability that the person chosen:
(i) is male,

....
[1]

(ii) is female and delivers on foot.

....
[1]

[Total 5 marks]

4 In a survey, 27 workers in an office were asked if they liked chocolate digestives, cookies and ginger biscuits. One person didn't like any of the biscuits. The results are shown in the Venn diagram.

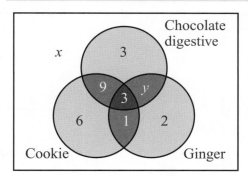

a) What are the values of x and y that should be used to complete the diagram?

$x = $ ...., $y = $ ....
[2]

b) What is the probability that a worker, chosen at random, likes ginger biscuits?

....
[2]

c) What is the probability that a worker, chosen at random, likes cookies and chocolate digestives, but not ginger biscuits?

....
[2]

[Total 6 marks]

Exam Practice Tip

If you're given a two-way table or a Venn diagram showing numbers and asked to work out probabilities, you need to know the total number of items. In a two-way table, this is just the number in the bottom-right cell, but for a Venn diagram, you need to add up all the numbers — including the one outside the circles.

Score

21

Section Six — Probability

The Addition Law

1 Daphne has a box that contains three different flavours of crisps. It holds 3 packets of cheese & onion crisps, 5 packets of roast chicken crisps and 4 packets of salt & vinegar crisps.

a) Are the events 'selecting cheese & onion crisps', 'selecting roast chicken crisps' and 'selecting salt & vinegar crisps' mutually exclusive? Explain your answer.

....

....

[2]

b) Daphne selects a packet from the box at random. Find the probability that Daphne selects:
(i) roast chicken crisps,

....

[1]

(ii) cheese & onion crisps or salt & vinegar crisps.

....

[1]

[Total 4 marks]

2 For the events A and B, P(A) = 0.45, P(B) = 0.35 and P(A and B) = 0.08.

a) Are events A and B mutually exclusive? Explain your answer.

.... P(A and B) is   not   0   so no?...

....

[2]

b) Find P(A or B).

....

[2]

[Total 4 marks]

3 Carmella picks a card at random from a standard pack of 52 cards.
What is the probability that she picks a jack or a spade?

> Work out P(jack), P(spade)
> and P(jack and spade), then
> use the general addition law.

....

[Total 3 marks]

Score:

11

Independent Events

1 The probabilities that Katie and Daniel will go to France this summer are 0.6 and 0.3 respectively. The probability that both Katie and Daniel go to France is 0.18.

    a) Are the events 'Katie goes to France' and 'Daniel goes to France' independent? Explain your answer.

    ....

    ....

    [2]

    b) Find the probability that only one of Katie and Daniel will go to France this summer.

    You want to find P(only K) or P(only D), which don't include P(K and D) — you might want to sketch a Venn diagram to help work out what you're looking for.

    ....

    [2]

    [Total 4 marks]

2 Ore is baking cakes. The probability of him leaving a cake in the oven too long is always 0.15.

If he bakes six cakes, what is the probability that he leaves at least one of the cakes in the oven too long? Give your answer to 3 significant figures.

....

[Total 3 marks]

3 Events A and B are independent. P(A) = 0.35 and P(B) = 0.4.

    a) Draw a fully-labelled Venn diagram to show the probabilities of events A and B.

    [3]

    b) Hence or otherwise, find P(A or B).

    ....

    [2]

    [Total 5 marks]

Score:

12

Tree Diagrams

1   A cricket match is scheduled to be played over a weekend. The probability that play will have to be stopped on Saturday due to poor weather conditions is 0.3. The probability that play will have to be stopped on Sunday is 0.4.

    a)   Draw a tree diagram to show this information.

[2]

    b)   Find the probability that play is stopped on both days.

....

[1]

    c)   Find the probability that play is stopped on exactly 1 day.

....

[2]

[Total 5 marks]

2   The Grizebeck Greys and the Broughton Blues play two football matches. The tree diagram below shows the probabilities of the different outcomes for each of the matches.

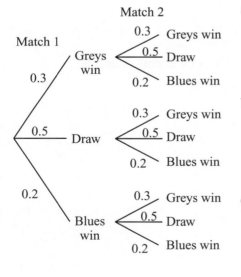

    a)   Calculate the probability that the Blues will win both the matches.

....

[1]

    b)   What is the probability that the same team will win both of the matches?

....

[2]

    c)   Calculate the probability that the teams will draw in one or both of the matches.

....

[2]

[Total 5 marks]

Exam Practice Tip

To find the probability of an end result from a tree diagram, just multiply along the branches. If you want the total probability of more than one end result, add up the relevant probabilities (and remember, sometimes it's easier to find the probability of the thing you want <u>not</u> happening, then subtract it from 1).

Score

10

Conditional Probability

1 This table shows the results of a survey asking 230 people what their favourite type of music is.

Find the probability that a randomly chosen person from the survey:

a) is male given that they prefer pop music,

	Hip-Hop	Rock	Pop	Total
Male	35	45	30	110
Female	48	31	41	120
Total	83	76	71	230

....
[2]

b) prefers hip-hop given that they are female.

....
[2]

[Total 4 marks]

2 Eight cards each have a different letter of the alphabet printed on them, as shown below.

The cards are shuffled and a card is picked at random and not replaced. Another card is then picked at random.

A E I O U P Q R

a) Find the probability that the second card picked is a consonant, given that the first card picked is a vowel.

....
[2]

b) Complete the tree diagram showing the probabilities of each card being a vowel or consonant.

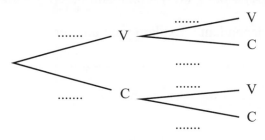

[3]

c) Calculate the probability that the second card picked is a vowel. Show your working.

....
[2]

The eight cards are reshuffled. Four cards are picked out randomly, one after the other, without replacement.

d) Calculate the probability that the first consonant picked out is the 4th card.

....
[3]

[Total 10 marks]

Section Six — Probability

3 A survey was carried out to find out what types of sport people watch on the TV. The Venn diagram below shows the results.

a) Find the probability that a randomly selected person watches cricket, given that they watch football.

....

[2]

b) Find the probability that a randomly selected person watches football and cricket given that they watch athletics.

....

[2]

[Total 4 marks]

4 Uma's horse is four times more likely to win a race if the ground is dry than if the ground is wet. The probability of her horse winning if the ground is wet is 0.12. The probability of the ground being dry at any race is 0.6.

Given that Uma's horse won the race, find the probability that the ground was dry. Give your answer to 3 s.f.

A tree diagram will be a big help in this question.

....

[Total 4 marks]

5 For the events A and B, P(A) = 0.35, P(B) = 0.28 and P(A|B) = 0.25.

a) Are events A and B independent? Explain your answer.

....

....

[2]

b) Find P(A and B).

....

[2]

c) Hence find P(B|A).

....

[2]

[Total 6 marks]

Exam Practice Tip

Even if the question doesn't ask for it, it's often a good idea to quickly sketch a tree diagram or a Venn diagram for conditional probability questions. Make sure you're comfortable with the notation as well — P(A|B) is the probability of A happening, given that B has happened (and vice versa for P(B|A)).

Score

28

The Binomial Distribution

1   A biased coin is tossed five times. The probability of it landing on heads on any one toss is $\frac{1}{3}$.

   a)   Write down one condition that must be met in order to model the number
         of times the coin lands on heads using a binomial distribution.

   ....

   ....

   [1]

   b)   Calculate, to 3 decimal places, the probability that the coin lands on heads at least twice.

   ....

   [5]

   c)   A different biased coin is also tossed five times. It is expected that it will land on heads
         exactly four times. What is the probability of it landing on heads on any one toss?

   ....

   [2]

   [Total 8 marks]

2   It is known that, on average, 65% of all trains arriving at a station are on time.
     The number of trains which arrive on time can be modelled by B(n, p).

   a)   Write down the value of p.

   p = ...

   [1]

   b)   Ten trains arrive at the station. Find the probability that exactly three of these are **not** on time.
         Give your answer correct to 3 significant figures.

   ....

   [3]

   c)   If the probability that all the trains arriving in one particular hour are on time is greater
         than 0.2, find the greatest number of trains that can arrive at the station in that hour.

   *Work out what the probability of all
   the trains being on time is in terms
   of n. Then try different values of n
   to find the right probability.*

   ....

   [3]

   [Total 7 marks]

Exam Practice Tip

Make sure you know how your calculator can help you with binomial distribution questions. If it has a
binomial probability function, use it — but make sure you still show all your working (i.e. which probability
it is that you're working out). If it doesn't then you'll need to know how to use your ^nC_r button.

Score

☐

15

 ☐   ☐   ☐

Higher

The Normal Distribution

1 A factory produces tins of butter beans. The weights, w, are known to be normally distributed. The mean weight of the tins is 418 g and the standard deviation is 0.7 g.

    a) 95% of the weights satisfy the inequality $a < w < b$. Find the values of a and b.

$a =$ .... $b =$ ....

[2]

The factory finds that the weight of butter beans it produces each day has a mean of 1000 kg and a standard deviation of 90 kg.

    b) One year the factory operates for 300 days. On how many of these days would you expect the weight of butter beans produced to be less than 910 kg?

....

[3]

[Total 5 marks]

2 Serena is investigating the planes that have landed at her local airfield in the last year. For each plane, she records the length (in m), the wingspan (in m) and the age (in whole years).

    a) Explain why the ages of the planes cannot be modelled by a normal distribution.

....

[1]

    b) The lengths of the planes can be modelled by $N(40, 8.5^2)$ and the wingspans can be modelled by $N(35, 11^2)$.

       The graph of the distribution of the lengths has been drawn on the right.

       On the same set of axes, sketch the graph of the distribution of the wingspans.

[2]

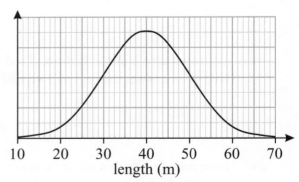
length (m)

    c) Find the probability that a randomly selected plane will have a wingspan of between 13 m and 57 m.

....

[3]

[Total 6 marks]

Quality Assurance

1 A manufacturer uses quality assurance to check that the waist sizes of skirts being produced are the required 60 cm. A sample is taken regularly and the mean is calculated and recorded.

a) Give one reason why the manufacturer performs the process of quality assurance.

....

....

[1]

b) Explain why the manufacturer uses sample means instead of collected data values to determine whether the skirts meet the requirements.

....

....

[1]

[Total 2 marks]

2 A machine is used to make shoelaces that are 55 cm long. Samples, each consisting of three measurements, are taken each hour from the machine.

Time	Lengths (cm)		
13:00	55.2	55.5	54.6
14:00	55.0	54.2	55.2
15:00	54.1	55.5	54.6
16:00	55.2	56.0	55.2
17:00	56.1	54.9	55.3
18:00	55.5	54.5	53.7

a) Plot the sample ranges on the control chart below.

Watch out — it's the sample <u>ranges</u>, not the means, that you're interested in this time.

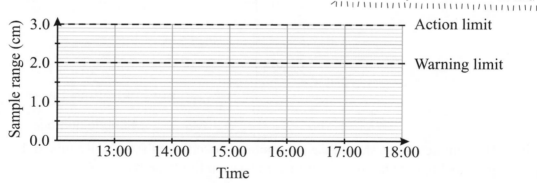

[2]

b) Explain why no lower action or warning limits are needed on this chart.

....

....

[1]

c) Do you think the machine is functioning properly? Justify your answer.

....

....

[1]

[Total 4 marks]

3 A machine puts matches into matchboxes. For quality assurance, a sample of 3 matchboxes is taken every 30 minutes and the mean number of matches in the sample calculated. The graph shows the results over 4 hours.

a) What percentage of the sample means would you **expect** to be outside the interval 19-21?

.... %
[1]

b) Find the standard deviation of the sample means if the machine was working properly.

....
[2]

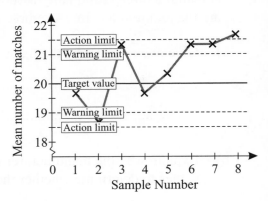

c) Describe what action is needed after the eighth sample was taken.

....
[1]

[Total 4 marks]

4 A company produces tins of spaghetti hoops. Every 30 minutes a sample of 4 tins is taken and the mean weight of the tins calculated. The target mean is 400 g.

a) The ninth sample has tins with the following weights: 400.9 g, 401.8 g, 401.5 g, 402.2 g. Calculate the sample mean and then complete the quality control chart below.

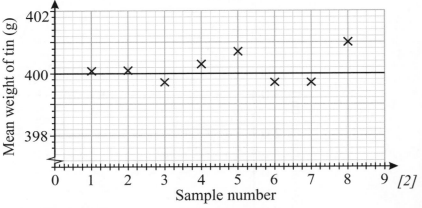

[2]

b) The sample means should have a standard deviation of 0.6 g. Use this to draw and label upper and lower warning and action limits on the graph.

[3]

c) Describe and explain what action should have been taken, and when.

....

....
[2]

[Total 7 marks]

Score:

17

Section Seven — Probability Distributions

Answers

Section One — Planning Data Collection

Page 4: Planning an Investigation

1 a) E.g. Users had fewer spots after using the new treatment for one month than they did after using the previous treatment for one month *[1 mark for a sensible hypothesis]*.

   b) E.g. There could be ethical issues when testing the acne products — they might cause harm to someone. / Acne is a sensitive subject — people might not want to talk about their spots. / It could be quite inconvenient to test because it's difficult to measure acne *[1 mark for a sensible answer]*.
   Other possible constraints you could talk about include time, costs and confidentiality.

2 Any three from:
   Planning — e.g. measure distances rounded to the nearest 0.1 km, because there will be a large range of distances travelled.
   Collecting data — e.g. collect primary data, because Safia knows it should be reliable.
   Processing and presenting — e.g. plot two histograms for Year 7 and Year 11 students. Then it's easy to compare their distributions.
   Interpreting — e.g. compare means, so you can see if the distance travelled to school by Year 11 students is greater than the distance travelled to school by Year 7 students.
   Evaluating — e.g. she might choose to use back-to-back stem and leaf diagrams, because she can display both sets of data at the same time for comparison.
   [6 marks available — 1 mark for each sensible example referring a stage of the statistical enquiry cycle up to 3 marks (answer must include more than one stage), 1 mark for each sensible reason up to 3 marks]
   There are loads of answers that will get the marks — make sure your examples refer to more than one stage and each has a sensible reason.

Page 5: Types of Data

1 a) Qualitative *[1 mark]*
   b) Discrete *[1 mark]*

2 a) Any item of data that cannot be measured numerically — e.g. types of music, types of format sold (CD, DVD, etc.) or names of customers *[1 mark]*.
   b) Any item of data that can be measured numerically — e.g. takings for each day, prices of CDs, or amounts spent by customers *[1 mark]*.

3 Ordinal scale *[1 mark]*

4 Bivariate *[1 mark]* and qualitative *[1 mark]*

Page 6: Simplifying and Grouping Data

1 a) 0, 6, 11 or 16 *[1 mark]*
   b) 0-5 coins class width: $6 - 0 = 6$
   16-30 class width: $31 - 16 = 15$
   [1 mark for both class widths correct]

2 a) E.g.

Age	1-10	11-20	21-30	31-40	41-50	51-60
Frequency	5	10	5	5	3	2

   [2 marks available — 1 mark for suitable age groups, 1 mark for all frequencies correct]
   You might have chosen different groups — as long as they're sensible and your frequencies are correct, you'll get the marks.

   b) Advantage: e.g. the data is easier to read and process. / You can see patterns and compare the groups.
   [1 mark for any sensible answer]
   Disadvantage: e.g. you lose some accuracy of the data. / Calculations such as the mean are only estimates.
   [1 mark for any sensible answer]

3 Rounding 21.98 cm to the nearest 0.1 cm gives 22.0 cm *[1 mark]*. This distorts the data because the rounded value goes in the $22 \leq l < 24$ class, but the actual value goes in the $20 \leq l < 22$ class *[1 mark]*.

Page 7: Data Sources

1 a) Primary data *[1 mark]*
   b) Secondary data *[1 mark]*

2 a) Primary data is data that you have collected yourself *[1 mark]*, whereas secondary data is data that someone else has collected *[1 mark]*.
   b) (i) Any one from:
        E.g. He can be sure that he collects the data he needs for his investigation. / He knows how reliable the data is.
        [1 mark for any sensible answer]
      (ii) Any one from:
        E.g. It's quicker and cheaper to get data. / It might be easier to get hold of. / The data set could be larger than he could collect on his own.
        [1 mark for any sensible answer]

3 a) Any two from:
      E.g. It might be in the wrong format. / It might be out of date. / There might not be any relevant data available. / It might be biased or unreliable.
      [2 marks available — 1 mark for each sensible answer]
   b) E.g. Julia might have difficulty getting access to the television presenters. / They might not want to tell Julia their salaries.
      [1 mark for any sensible answer]

Pages 8-9: Populations and Sampling

1 Census *[1 mark]*

2 a) Census data should be representative of the population it's drawn from *[1 mark]*.
   b) E.g. Taking a sample of people in the town would be quicker, cheaper and more practical than asking everyone.
      [1 mark for any sensible answer]
   c) E.g. The phone book might not cover the whole population — only choosing names from the phone book excludes people who are ex-directory or who don't own a telephone.
      [1 mark for any sensible answer]

3 a) All the supporters of the football club *[1 mark]*.
      Be careful here — it's the supporters, not the town population, that the football club is interested in.
   b) All people on the electoral register of the town *[1 mark]*.
   c) E.g. Not everyone on the electoral register will support the football club. / Some supporters may not be on the electoral register (because they're too young, live elsewhere or aren't registered to vote).
      [1 mark for any sensible answer]

4 a) Advantage: using a sample is quicker / cheaper / the only practical option for this situation.
      [1 mark for any sensible answer]
      Disadvantage: the sample could be less accurate / it might be biased *[1 mark for any sensible answer]*.
   b) E.g. It would be difficult and impractical/impossible for her to be sure that she had investigated every single deer in the UK.
      [1 mark for any sensible answer]

5 a) All the cakes baked that day *[1 mark]*.
   b) E.g. Cakes are used up (i.e. eaten) when they are sampled.
      [1 mark for any sensible answer]

6 a) The map of the county with all the lakes on. / A list of all the lakes on the map *[1 mark]*.

b) E.g. It's not appropriate. The lakes in the county may not be representative of others in the rest of the UK. The environmental group's sample only covered lakes, not rivers.
[3 marks available — 1 mark for not appropriate, 1 mark for each sensible reason up to 2 marks]

Pages 10-12: Sampling Techniques

1 Number the names in the list from 1 to 4000 *[1 mark]*. Use a computer, calculator, random number table, dice or cards to generate 500 different random numbers between 1 and 4000 *[1 mark]*. Match the 500 random numbers to the numbered list of names to choose the sample *[1 mark]*.

2 Number all the items in the list *[1 mark]*. Since $700 \div 50 = 14$ *[1 mark]*, pick a random starting point between 1 and 14 using a computer, calculator, random number table, dice or cards. Then sample every 14th item after that *[1 mark]*.
E.g. If the random starting point is 4, then you'd sample the 4th, 18th, 32nd, … etc. items.

3 a) Each primary school in England could be a cluster *[1 mark]*. So randomly select a sample of primary schools from the list and survey every teacher in those schools *[1 mark]*.

b) E.g. The primary schools are spread over a wide area, so cluster sampling could reduce costs for the textbook company *[1 mark]*.

4 a) Opportunity (or convenience) sampling *[1 mark]*

b) Mo's sampling method is appropriate *[1 mark]*. The year groups might give different results — e.g. Year 11 students might be more likely to wear make-up than Year 7 students. *[1 mark for any sensible reason]*.

5 a) Judgement sample *[1 mark]*
The news reporter is using their judgement (based on people wearing the team's football shirt) to choose who to interview.

b) E.g. The news reporter could be unreliable or biased (e.g. by choosing to interview only men) *[1 mark for any sensible reason]*.

c) E.g. The reporter might not have a list of the whole population of the team's fans to sample *[1 mark for any sensible reason]*.

6 a) Researcher A uses quota sampling *[1 mark]* and Researcher B uses opportunity (or convenience) sampling *[1 mark]*.

b) Advantage: e.g. it's fairly quick to do / it gives representation to different groups / members of the sample can be easily replaced by ones with the same characteristics if they refuse / it can be done without a sampling frame.
[1 mark for any sensible answer]
Disadvantage: e.g. it's easily biased / the researcher may be biased / people who refuse to answer may have similar views.
[1 mark for any sensible answer]

7 a) Number all the springs 1 to 5000 *[1 mark]*.
Since $5000 \div 100 = 50$ *[1 mark]*, select a starting point at random between 1 and 50 using a computer, calculator, random number table, dice or cards.
Then sample every 50th spring after that *[1 mark]*.
E.g. If the random starting point is 12, then you'd sample the 12th, 62nd, 112th, … etc. springs.

b) The interval might coincide with a pattern — e.g. if every 50th spring the machine makes is faulty, either all springs will be faulty or none will *[1 mark]*.

8 Fred's sample is non-random and doesn't fairly represent the whole population *[1 mark]*. People passing through a bus station between 5.30 pm and 6.30 pm on a Monday are more likely to be commuters that use public transport *[1 mark]*.

9 E.g. Number all the cakes from 1 to 50 reading across each row. Choose the first 5 numbers reading across the random number table, and take the last two digits from each number. Ignore any numbers that are outside the range 1-50 or repeated. The random numbers are 09, 16, 37, 32, 15.

Match the random numbers to the cake weights — the cake weights are 203 g, 198 g, 201 g, 195 g, 189 g.
[4 marks available — 1 mark for numbering the cakes, 1 mark for describing how to use the random number table, 1 mark for correctly choosing 5 random numbers from the table, 1 mark for matching the random numbers to the correct weights]

10 a) Any one from:
E.g. The groups are well defined, so the sample should be representative of the population. / You can compare results from the different groups *[1 mark for any sensible answer]*.

b) Total number of members:
$271 + 277 + 45 + 38 + 39 + 18 = 688$ *[1 mark]*
Female golfers: $(271 \div 688) \times 40 = 15.7...$
Male golfers: $(277 \div 688) \times 40 = 16.1...$
Female swimmers: $(45 \div 688) \times 40 = 2.6...$
Male swimmers: $(38 \div 688) \times 40 = 2.2...$
Female tennis players: $(39 \div 688) \times 40 = 2.2...$
Male tennis players: $(18 \div 688) \times 40 = 1.0...$
[1 mark for the correct method, 1 mark for at least one calculation correct]
Rounding to the nearest whole number, the sample looks like:

	Golfers	Swimmers	Tennis players
Female	16	3	2
Male	16	2	1

[2 marks for all six correct or 1 mark for three to five correct]

Section Two — Collecting Data

Pages 13-14: Questionnaires

1 Any two from:
E.g. There is no time period specified, so some people may say how many books they read in a month, and some may say how many they read in a year. / The classes overlap — e.g. if someone had read 5 books, they could tick either the first or the second box. / For someone who doesn't read at all (i.e. reads 0 books), there is no box to tick.
[2 marks available — 1 mark for each sensible answer, up to a total of 2 marks]

2 a) E.g. The question is ambiguous — 'a lot of money' could mean different things to different people. / Some people might find this a sensitive question so may not answer it truthfully.
[1 mark for a sensible comment]
E.g. How much did you spend on Christmas presents last year? Then give options: £0-£29.99, £30.00-£59.99, £60.00-£89.99, £90+ *[1 mark for a suitable question]*.
Your question might be phrased slightly differently, and you might have chosen different ranges of values (or none at all), but as long as your question is sensible, you'll get the mark.

b) E.g. It's a leading question as it suggests reality TV is bad, which might make you more likely to agree.
[1 mark for a sensible comment]
E.g. Do you enjoy watching reality TV programmes? Rank your answer from 1 ('strongly dislike') to 5 ('strongly like') *[1 mark for a suitable question]*.
You don't have to use a numerical scale here — you could give different options in words to choose from, or you could leave it as an open question so people can write whatever they want.

3 a) Advantage: E.g. It's easy to reach a large area (the students could come from anywhere in the country). / Sending questionnaires out by post is a fairly cheap way to distribute them. / Respondents are more likely to be truthful.
[1 mark for any sensible answer]
Disadvantage: E.g. The students may have moved so the addresses might be out of date. / They have no way of knowing if the questionnaires actually reach their intended recipient. / There could be a lot of non-responses. / Recipients might not understand the questions. *[1 mark for any sensible answer]*

Answers

b) Any two from:
E.g. They could offer an incentive to respond to the questionnaire (e.g. a free gift or entry into a prize draw). / They could follow up people that haven't responded to the questionnaire. / Provide stamped addressed envelopes to make it easy (and free) to return the questionnaires.
[2 marks available — 1 mark for each sensible suggestion, up to a total of 2 marks]

4 a) A pilot study is when you test your questionnaire on a small group before sending it out to the full sample *[1 mark]*.

b) Any two from:
E.g. A pilot study helps spot any problems with the questions — e.g. if they are unclear or ambiguous. / It's quicker, easier and cheaper to fix any problems with the questionnaire at this stage. / You can check that your distribution and collection methods work before distributing it to a large number of people. / If the pilot study has an unexpected outcome, you can change your investigation or hypothesis to take this into account.
[2 marks available — 1 mark for each sensible suggestion, up to a total of 2 marks]

c) E.g. To what extent do you agree with the following statement? "The school library has a wide selection of books."
Choose from the following options:
Strongly disagree/disagree/no opinion/agree/strongly agree.
[2 marks available — 1 mark for a suitable statement/ question about the library, 1 mark for a sensible range of opinions to choose from]

5 a) It is a sensitive question, which students might not want to answer/might not answer truthfully, so a random response technique is suitable *[1 mark for any sensible answer]*.

b) You'd expect about $1000 \times 0.5 = 500$ students to have answered yes because their coin showed heads *[1 mark]*.
So 500 of the yes answers can be ignored.
This leaves $632 - 500 = 132$ *[1 mark]* out of the remaining 500 people who have actually answered yes to the question.
So an estimate of the proportion of students who eat at least one bar of chocolate every day is
$(132 \div 500) \times 100 = 26.4\%$ *[1 mark]*.

Page 15: Interviews

1 E.g. People who have knowingly broken the law are likely to lie about it to an interviewer *[1 mark for any sensible answer]*.

2 Advantage: e.g. They can ask open questions in an interview, and ask follow-up questions if they need the interviewee to clarify or expand on answers. / They will get a higher response rate from an interview. / They can adapt their questions to suit the interviewee (e.g. if talking to a younger person, they might want to ask slightly different questions) *[1 mark for any sensible advantage]*.
Disadvantage: e.g. Face-to-face interviews take a long time to carry out, whereas an online questionnaire won't take long to organise. / Face-to-face interviews can be expensive, whereas online questionnaires are very cheap. / They can get answers from a larger range of areas using an online questionnaire.
[1 mark for any sensible disadvantage]

3 a) Any two from:
E.g. Face-to-face interviews allow you to ask more complex questions. / The response rate for interviews tends to be higher than for questionnaires. / The interviewer can be sure the correct person is answering the questions (whereas a questionnaire could be filled in by anyone). /
The interviewer can ask follow-up questions if needed.
[2 marks available — 1 mark for each sensible advantage, up to a total of 2 marks]

b) Any two from:
E.g. It's a lot cheaper and easier to sample a large area over the phone than in person. / It's easier to survey a larger sample because it's quicker to phone round people than travel to interview them. / If someone is out when the interviewer phones them, they can phone back later (which might not be practical with a face-to-face interview).
[2 marks available — 1 mark for each sensible advantage, up to a total of 2 marks]

Page 16: Observation and Reference Sources

1 E.g.

Sport	Tally	Frequency
Football		
Rugby		
Tennis		
Other		

[2 marks available — 1 mark for columns (or rows) for Sport, Tally and Frequency, 1 mark for rows (or columns) for a sensible range of sport options, including an 'other' option]
You might have included 'BMX biking' as an option — here, it's covered by the 'Other' option.

2 a) Any two from:
E.g. The data could be out of date. / Some information could be missing. / The data could be unreliable. / The data could already have been rounded or processed in some way.
[2 marks available — 1 mark for each sensible answer, up to a total of 2 marks]

b) Any one from:
E.g. It gives Kendra access to a large amount of data that she would not be able to collect herself. / The data is from the Office for National Statistics, so it should be fairly reliable *[1 mark for any sensible answer]*.

c)

Country	Tally	Frequency
Spain		
France		
Italy		
Republic of Ireland		
USA		
Other		

[2 marks available — 1 mark for columns (or rows) for Country, Tally and Frequency, 1 mark for rows (or columns) for a sensible range of country options, including 'Other']
It's important to include the 'Other' option here — just because these are the most popular destinations, it doesn't mean everyone will have gone to one of these countries.

Pages 17-18: Experiments

1 a) Explanatory variable: volume of music *[1 mark]*
Response variable: driving speed *[1 mark]*

b) Any two from:
E.g. the type of car driven / the age of the driver / the gender of the driver / the weather conditions / the driver's normal driving habits (e.g. if they're likely to speed) / the type of music being listened to.
[2 marks available — 1 mark for each sensible answer, up to a total of 2 marks]

c) E.g. To make sure that any changes in the response variable are due to changes in the explanatory variable only
[1 mark for any sensible answer].

2 Any one from:
E.g. The children may behave differently in a laboratory. / They may feel stressed, making the experiment unethical
[1 mark for any sensible answer].

3 a) Any one from:
E.g. Field experiments let you see how people behave in a real-life environment. / The scientist still has some control over the variables, but the conditions are more realistic *[1 mark for any sensible answer]*.

b) Any one from:
E.g. The scientist has less control over the extraneous variables. / Field experiments are less reliable and less valid than lab experiments *[1 mark for any sensible answer]*.

c) Any one from:
E.g. The number of other people around (e.g. people might be more likely to obey if there are other people nearby). / The age or gender of participants might affect their reactions *[1 mark for any sensible answer]*.

4 a) E.g. He could make the students sit a test just before the summer holidays, then make them sit a test just after the summer holidays. The tests should be the same or similar, so he can reliably compare the results for the two tests.
[2 marks available — 1 mark for stating that the students should sit two tests (before and after the holidays) 1 mark for stating that the tests should be the same or similar]

b) Any one from:
E.g. He has only sampled a small number of students, so his results may not be reliable. / He has no control over any extraneous variables (e.g. whether students studied or not over the summer holidays) *[1 mark for any sensible answer]*.

5 a) Experimental group: group A
Control group: group B *[1 mark for both]*

b) Matched pairs are two people who are as similar as possible. One person from each pair is put into the experimental group and the other person is put into the control group.
[2 marks available — 1 mark for stating that the pairs need to be similar, 1 mark for stating that one person is put into each group]
For the doctor's experiment you'd probably want the matched pairs to have similar lifestyles, be the same gender and have similar weights and ages.

c) E.g. Using matched pairs reduces the variability caused by other factors, so that the doctor can be more confident that any differences in cholesterol levels are due to her pill, not extraneous factors *[1 mark for any sensible answer]*.

Page 19: Simulation

1 a) E.g. Take the 1st (or 2nd or 3rd) digit of each number and use that as the result of a spin, ignoring the digits 0, 6, 7, 8 and 9.
[2 marks available — 2 marks for a fully correct method, otherwise 1 mark for not stating all the omissions]
There are lots of different ways of generating a sample from a random number table. You'd get the marks for any correct method.

b) Using the first digit of each number in the table (ignoring 0 and 6-9) gives 3, 4, 5, 3, 1, 1, 2, so it will take 7 spins to win the game.
OR Using the second digit of each number in the table (ignoring 0 and 6-9) gives 5, 4, 2, 3, 2, 4, 1, so it will take 7 spins to win the game.
OR Using the third digit of each number in the table (ignoring 0 and 6-9) gives 1, 5, 1, 4, 3, 2, so it will take 6 spins to win the game.
[1 mark for the correct number of spins needed to win, using the method described in part a)]

c) To improve the reliability of your estimation, run the simulation more times and find the average number of spins needed to win *[1 mark]*.

2 $42 + 14 + 13 + 31 = 100$, so assign the numbers 1 to 100 to the different films (so the first 42 numbers are assigned to Superheroes!, the next 14 numbers are assigned to Song of the Mermen, etc.): 1-42 = Superheroes!, 43-56 = Song of the Mermen, 57-69 = 15 Days at Sea, 70-100 = The Devil's Confidante. Generate five random numbers from the table — e.g. read across the table from left to right, using the last two digits from each number and counting '00' as '100'.
The numbers are 86, 78, 07, 99, 37. Match the random numbers to the films. So, according to the simulation, the next five people will go to see 86 = The Devil's Confidante, 78 = The Devil's Confidante, 07 = Superheroes!, 99 = The Devil's Confidante, 37 = Superheroes!
[3 marks available — 1 mark for assigning numbers to films, 1 mark for generating random numbers from table, 1 mark for matching numbers to films]
If you'd used the first two digits of the numbers in the table, you'd get 58, 27, 60, 29 and 53 — so the films would be 15 Days at Sea, Superheroes!, 15 Days at Sea, Superheroes! and Song of the Mermen.

Page 20: Problems with Collected Data

1 a) (i) Any three from:
• He could correct/remove the mistake in the age column — no one can be 190 years old.
• He could correct the mistakes in the country column — London and New York are cities, not countries.
• He could make sure all the measurements are in the same units — e.g. holiday lengths in days (some are in weeks) and temperature in °C (not °F).
• He could correct the row for Spain — the temperature and the length of the holiday are the wrong way round.
• He could fill in the missing data in the temperature row/ remove that row entirely.
[3 marks available — 1 mark for each correction, up to a total of 3 marks]

(ii) E.g. The data should be more reliable after cleaning, as the travel agent can be sure that he's corrected most of the data properly — e.g. he can find out which countries the cities are in, convert the times in weeks to days and temperatures in °F to °C, find out the average temperature for New York and swap the entries that are the wrong way round.
[2 marks available — 1 mark for stating that the data will be more reliable, 1 mark for a sensible explanation]
Sometimes, the cleaned data might be unreliable — for example, if there's lots of missing data, or if it's not possible to work out how to correct mistakes. But in this case, he should be able to clean the data pretty well.

b) (i) Any one from:
E.g. People are unlikely to have recorded the average temperature while they were away, so would not be able to fill in the final column. / It is an online questionnaire and some people might not have access to the internet. / If a group of people had been on holiday together, all their results would be the same, which might influence any conclusions. / Some people's holiday might have included more than one country
[1 mark for any sensible answer]

(ii) Any one from:
E.g. Group ages into classes that people can select from. / Provide a list of drop-down options for the countries so that people cannot enter cities by mistake. / Specify the units for the length of holiday (e.g. days) and temperature (e.g. °C) so that people know the format he wants
[1 mark for any sensible answer]

Section Three — Representing Data

Page 21: Frequency Tables

1 a)

Pool balls left	0	1	2	3	4	5	6	7
Tally	JHT I	IIII	III	III	I	I	I	II
Frequency	6	4	3	3	1	1	1	2

[2 marks available — 1 mark for correct tally row, 1 mark for a frequency row that matches the tally row]

b) 6 + 4 + 3 + 3 + 1 + 1 + 1 + 2 = 21 games *[1 mark]*

c) There are 1 + 1 + 2 = 4 games where Zoe has 5 or more pool balls left (i.e. 5, 6 or 7), so she loses 4 points *[1 mark]*.

2 a) 14 days *[1 mark]*

b)

No. of birds	0	1	2	3	4	5	6	7	8	9
Tally			I	II	IIII	II	II	II	I	
Frequency	0	0	1	2	4	2	2	2	1	0

[2 marks available — 1 mark for correct tally row, 1 mark for a frequency row that matches the tally row]

c) mode = 4 birds *[1 mark]*

d) 3 + 8 + 5 + 7 + 4 + 3 + 2 + 6 + 4 + 7 + 5 + 4 + 4 + 6 *[1 mark]* = 68 birds *[1 mark]*
You could also find this out using your frequency table — i.e. work out (2 × 1) + (3 × 2) + ... + (8 × 1) = 68 birds.

Page 22: Grouped Frequency Tables

1 a) E.g.

Age	Under 10	10-19	20-29	30-39	40 and above
Tally	JHT	JHT JHT JHT	IIII	II	JHT I
Frequency	5	15	4	2	6

[3 marks available — 1 mark for choosing suitable age groups that don't overlap, 1 mark for correct tally row, 1 mark for a frequency row that matches the tally row]
You'd still get the marks if you used different age groups, as long as your tallies and frequencies are correct.

b) 15 + 4 + 2 + 6 = 27 *[1 mark]*

2 a)

Time	$5.0 < t \le 6.0$	$6.0 < t \le 7.0$	$7.0 < t \le 8.0$	$8.0 < t \le 9.0$
Tally	JHT JHT II	JHT III	JHT	JHT
Frequency	12	8	5	5

[2 marks available — 1 mark for correct tally row, 1 mark for a frequency row that matches the tally row]

b) 12 + 8 = 20 *[1 mark]*

c) E.g. Rounding 6.043 s to the nearest 0.1 seconds gives 6.0 s *[1 mark]*. The rounded time goes in the $5.0 < t \le 6.0$ class, whereas the actual time goes in the $6.0 < t \le 7.0$ class, which makes the table misleading *[1 mark]*.

Page 23: Two-Way Tables

1 a) 13 *[1 mark]*

b) 5 + 4 + 3 = 12 *[1 mark]*

c) E.g. This data supports the statement because there are more men who are over 1.9 m tall married to women who are over 1.8 m tall than men who are over 1.9 m tall married to women who are less than 1.8 m tall *[1 mark]*.

2 a)

	Black	Red	Yellow	Green	Total
Adults	6	2	11 − 6 − 2 − 3 = 0	3	11
Children	1	9 − 2 = 7	3	6 − 3 = 3	1 + 7 + 3 + 3 = 14
Total	6 + 1 = 7	9	0 + 3 = 3	6	11 + 14 = 25

[2 marks available — 2 marks for all values correct, otherwise 1 mark for at least 4 values correct]
You could have done different calculations here, but the answers should be the same.

b) 3 + 6 = 9 people *[1 mark]*

c) There are 14 children and there's 1 child whose favourite colour is black, so 14 − 1 = 13 children *[1 mark]*.

Page 24: Interpreting Tables

1 a) Rabbit *[1 mark]*

b) E.g. The percentages in the table appear to have been rounded to 1 decimal place, whereas the total (100%) will use the unrounded values *[1 mark]*.

2 a) The missing values are (reading left to right):
90 + 160 + 300 + 120 + 40 + 70 = 780
90 + 130 + 300 + 150 + 60 + 80 = 810
[1 mark for both correct]

b) There is an increase in total flying hours between 1995 and 2014 *[1 mark]*.

c) The percentage for 2010-2014 is:
(150 ÷ 810) × 100 = 18.5% (1 d.p.) *[1 mark]*
So the proportion of hours flown by Type D helicopters was much higher in 2010-2014 than in 1995-1999 *[1 mark]*.

Pages 25-26: Bar Charts

1 a) 2.5 symbols represent 2.5 × 2 = 5 books *[1 mark]*

b) 4 symbols on Wednesday represent 4 × 2 = 8 books and 1.5 symbols on Tuesday represent 1.5 × 2 = 3 books. So the difference is 8 − 3 = 5 books *[1 mark]*.

c)

Friday	■ ■ ■ ■	*[1 mark]*

d) There are 3 symbols for Monday, so look for the day with 3 ÷ 2 = 1.5 symbols — Tuesday *[1 mark]*.

2 a) 60% *[1 mark]*

b) Widowed *[1 mark]*

c) The bar charts show percentages — they don't actually say how many males and females there are. / There's a higher proportion of married males but you don't know how many males and females there are in total. *[1 mark]*

3 a) The number of adults smoking has decreased for both genders from 2000 to 2018 *[1 mark]*.

b) 50 000 − 40 000 = 10 000 *[1 mark]*

c) From 2000 to 2018, the difference between numbers of men and women smoking has decreased *[1 mark]*.

4 a)

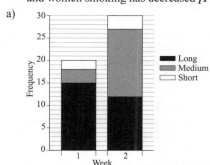

[2 marks available — 2 marks for all heights correct, otherwise 1 mark for correct height of at least one length of ride]

b) Any one from:
E.g. It's easy to compare total frequencies and individual categories. / The data is discrete and split into a small number of categories *[1 mark for any sensible reason]*.

Page 27: Stem and Leaf Diagrams

1 a)
```
3 | 1 2 7
4 | 3 4 5 5 5 8
5 | 0 2 2 9
6 | 1 6
7 | 0
```
Key:
3 | 1 = 31

[3 marks available — 1 mark for correct leaves on each stem, 1 mark for leaves in correct order, 1 mark for a suitable key]

b) modal score = 45 *[1 mark]*

c) range = 70 − 31 = 39 *[1 mark]*

2 a)

<u>Sven</u>   <u>Igor</u>
```
          12  10 | 2 | 50
50 32 18 12 06 | 3 | 16 24
    53 51 15 15 | 4 | 10 10 34 48 50
            31 | 5 | 21 25 32
```
Key: 10 | 2 = 2:10   Key: 2 | 50 = 2:50

[2 marks available — 1 mark for all values correct, 1 mark for a suitable key]

b) There are 12 tracks on Sven's album, so the median is halfway between the 6th and 7th values.
This is halfway between 3:32 and 3:50 *[1 mark]*, which is 3:41 or 3 minutes 41 seconds *[1 mark]*.

c) E.g. Igor's tracks are generally longer *[1 mark]*, because most of his data is towards the higher end of the distribution and Sven's data is fairly symmetrical about the middle of the distribution *[1 mark]*.
You'd get the marks if you said Igor's data is negatively skewed, whereas Sven's data is fairly symmetrical (or slightly positively skewed). You could also compare the medians by saying that Igor's median (= 4:34) is higher than Sven's median (= 3:41).

Page 28: Population Pyramids and Choropleth Maps

1 E.g. The south east (bottom right) corner of the map has the highest population *[1 mark]*, because those squares have the darkest shading *[1 mark]*.

2 a) 14% + 13% + 12% = 39% *[1 mark]*

b) 55-59 years *[1 mark]*
6% of people in Town B are aged 55-59 years compared to 3% of people in Town A.

c) E.g. People in Town B might have a higher life expectancy. / Town B might have lots of old people's homes, which would explain why there are more older people.
[1 mark for any sensible reason]

d) The population pyramid suggests that Town A has had a higher birth rate than Town B in the last 10 years *[1 mark]*. This is because Town A has a higher proportion of people aged 0-9, so a higher proportion of babies are likely to have been born in the last 10 years
[1 mark for any sensible explanation].

Page 29: Pie Charts

1 Calculate the size of the angle for each colour:
red = (3 ÷ 45) × 360° = 24°, blue = (12 ÷ 45) × 360° = 96°, green = (10 ÷ 45) × 360° = 80°, black = (5 ÷ 45) × 360° = 40° and other = (15 ÷ 45) × 360° = 120°
Draw this information in a pie chart with a radius of 1.5 cm.

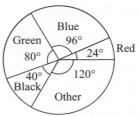

[4 marks available — 1 mark for correct method to find size of the angles, 1 mark for all angles calculated correctly, 1 mark for radius measuring 1.5 cm, 1 mark for all angles drawn correctly]

2 a) Angle for under-ripe = 360° − 45° − 60° − 90° = 165°

Condition	Frequency
Rotten	(45° ÷ 360°) × 960 = 120
Over-ripe	(60° ÷ 360°) × 960 = 160
Ripe	(90° ÷ 360°) × 960 = 240
Under-ripe	(165° ÷ 360°) × 960 = 440

[3 marks available — 1 mark for correct under-ripe angle, 1 mark for correct method, 1 mark for all frequencies correct]

b) E.g. The two diagrams don't support Johnny's statement *[1 mark]*, because you don't know the number of rotten oranges from the pie chart (only the proportion) *[1 mark]*.
Johnny would be correct if he said that there's a higher proportion of rotten oranges.

Page 30: Comparative Pie Charts

1 a) Tony *[1 mark]*
Both pie charts have the same angle for music but Tony spent more money overall (£50 to £30), so he spent more money on music.

b) Area of Jin's pie chart = $\pi r^2 = \pi \times 1.5^2 = 7.068...$ cm²
Area for £1 = 7.068... ÷ 30 = 0.235... cm² *[1 mark]*
Area of Tony's pie chart = 50 × 0.235... = 11.780... cm²
So for Tony's pie chart: $\pi r^2 = 11.780...$ *[1 mark]*,
⇒ $r^2 = 3.75$ ⇒ $r = 1.936... = 1.94$ cm (2 d.p.) *[1 mark]*
The diameter of Jin's pie chart is 3 cm, so the radius is 1.5 cm.

2 a) (i) Town A area = $\pi r^2 = \pi \times 2^2 = 12.56...$ cm²
Area for one person = 12.56... ÷ 2880 = 0.004... cm²
[1 mark]
Town B area = 3420 × 0.004... = 14.92...
So for Town B: $\pi r^2 = 14.92...$ *[1 mark]*
⇒ $r^2 = 4.75$ ⇒ $r = 2.17... = 2.2$ cm (1 d.p.) *[1 mark]*

(ii)

Distance	$0 \leq d < 2$	$2 \leq d < 5$	$5 \leq d < 10$
Freq.	1273	608	532
Angle	(1273 ÷ 3420) × 360° = 134°	(608 ÷ 3420) × 360° = 64°	(532 ÷ 3420) × 360° = 56°

Distance	$10 \leq d < 20$	$20 \leq d < 30$	$d \geq 30$
Freq.	475	247	285
Angle	(475 ÷ 3420) × 360° = 50°	(247 ÷ 3420) × 360° = 26°	(285 ÷ 3420) × 360° = 30°

[2 marks available — 2 marks for all angles correct, otherwise 1 mark for at least 3 angles correct]

(iii)

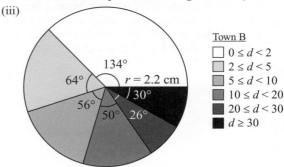

Town B
□ $0 \leq d < 2$
▨ $2 \leq d < 5$
▨ $5 \leq d < 10$
▨ $10 \leq d < 20$
▨ $20 \leq d < 30$
■ $d \geq 30$

[2 marks available — 1 mark for all angles drawn correctly, 1 mark for radius measuring 2.2 cm]

b) Similarity — e.g. the most common distance travelled to work by people in Town A and Town B is $0 \le d < 2$ km *[1 mark]*.
Difference — e.g. a greater proportion of people in Town B travel over 20 km to work *[1 mark]*.
There's loads of things you could say to get the marks here.

Page 31: Vertical Line Graphs & Frequency Polygons

1 a)

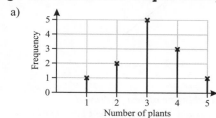

[2 marks available — 1 mark for using thin vertical lines, 1 mark for all line heights correct]

b) The plants' heights are continuous data and vertical line graphs are drawn for discrete data *[1 mark]*.

2 a)

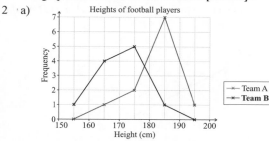

[2 marks available — 1 mark for all points plotted correctly, 1 mark for points joined up with straight lines]

b) E.g. The line for Team A's frequency polygon shows higher frequencies for taller heights and lower frequencies for shorter heights compared to the frequency polygon for Team B *[1 mark]*.

Page 32: Cumulative Frequency Diagrams

1 a)

No. of words	5	6	7	8	9	10	11
Frequency	2	5	6	3	2	1	1
Cumulative frequency	2	2 + 5 = 7	7 + 6 = 13	13 + 3 = 16	16 + 2 = 18	18 + 1 = 19	19 + 1 = 20

[2 marks available — 2 marks for all values correct, otherwise 1 mark for at least 4 values correct]

b)

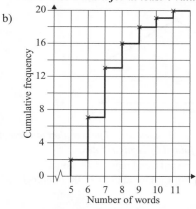

[2 marks available — 1 mark for all heights correct, 1 mark for 'steps' between values]

c) 19 *[1 mark]*

2 a) First work out the cumulative frequencies:

Time	$1.5 \le t < 2$	$2 \le t < 2.5$	$2.5 \le t < 3$	$3 \le t < 3.5$	$3.5 \le t < 4$
Frequency	1	4	5	1	0
Cum. freq.	1	1 + 4 = 5	5 + 5 = 10	10 + 1 = 11	11 + 0 = 11

Then plot the cumulative frequency against the highest value in each class:

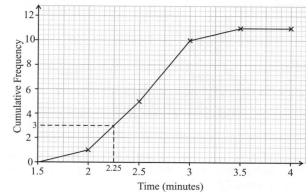

[4 marks available — 1 mark for all cumulative frequencies correct, 1 mark for heights of points correctly plotted, 1 mark for plotting at the highest value of each class, 1 mark for joining points with either straight lines or smooth curves]
You could've joined the points with a curve instead of straight lines.

b) Using the cumulative frequency graph, there are approximately 3 kettles that took less than 2.25 minutes to boil *[1 mark]*. So there are approximately $11 - 3 = 8$ kettles that took more than 2.25 minutes to boil *[1 mark]*.

Pages 33-34: Histograms

1 The first bar has frequency density 25, so the rest of the y-axis will be labelled 50, 75, 100. Then read off the frequency densities:

Speed (s km/h)	Freq. density
$30 < s \le 35$	25
$35 < s \le 40$	100
$40 < s \le 45$	55
$45 < s \le 50$	20

[2 marks available — 1 mark for all values in the table correct, otherwise 1 mark for at least one value correct]

2 a) Her data is continuous and grouped *[1 mark]*, so it can be shown on a histogram.

b)

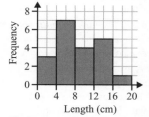

[3 marks available — 1 mark for correctly labelled axes, 1 mark for all bars the correct width, 1 mark for all bar heights correct. Lose 1 mark if the bars don't touch]

c) (i) An estimate would be the total frequencies of half of the $8 < l \le 12$ cm class and all of the $12 < l \le 16$ cm class. Using the table (or your histogram):
$(4 \div 2) + 5$ *[1 mark]* = 7 *[1 mark]*

(ii) It's an estimate because the data is grouped, so you don't know the exact data values *[1 mark]*.
For the estimate in part (i) you assumed that half of the $8 < l \le 12$ cm class measured between 10 and 12 cm.

3 a) Work out the frequency densities using frequency density = frequency ÷ class width.

Time	$0 < x \le 5$	$5 < x \le 10$	$10 < x \le 20$	$20 < x \le 50$
Freq.	4	10	18	15
Class width	5	5	10	30
Frequency density	4 ÷ 5 = 0.8	10 ÷ 5 = 2	18 ÷ 10 = 1.8	15 ÷ 30 = 0.5

Answers

88

Then draw the histogram:

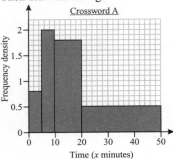
Crossword A

[5 marks available — 2 marks for all frequency densities correct, otherwise 1 mark for at least 2 frequency densities correct, 1 mark for correct labels on y-axis, 1 mark for all bar heights correct, 1 mark for all bar widths correct. Lose 1 mark if bars don't touch]
You might have labelled the y-axis from 0 to 4 to match the histogram for crossword B. You'd still get the marks as long as the frequency densities of the bars are correct.

b) An estimate would be all frequencies in the $0 < x \leq 5$ class, all of the $5 < x \leq 10$ class and half of the $10 < x \leq 20$ class. Using the table for crossword A:
$4 + 10 + (18 \div 2)$ *[1 mark]* = 23 *[1 mark]*
You could have answered this question using the histogram for crossword A: $(5 \times 0.8) + (5 \times 2) + ((10 \times 1.8) \div 2) = 23$.

c) The frequencies of the bars are represented by area:
$0 < x \leq 7$ bar = $7 \times 3 = 21$, $7 < x \leq 17$ bar = $10 \times 2.2 = 22$ and $17 < x \leq 25$ bar = $8 \times 0.5 = 4$.
The highest frequency is 22 (the bar has the largest area), so the modal class is $7 < x \leq 17$ minutes.
[2 marks available — 1 mark for correct modal class, 1 mark for a suitable explanation]
Sometimes you can tell which bar has the largest area just by looking, but work out the areas if you're unsure.

d) It's not appropriate to compare them, because they have different class intervals / different frequency density scales / different time scales *[1 mark for any sensible answer]*.

Page 35: The Shape of a Distribution

1 a) Company A median = £45 000
Company B median = £36 250 *[1 mark for both correct]*
Most of company B's data is towards the lower end of the distribution, so it has a lower median than company A.

b) The salaries for company A are fairly symmetrical around the median of £45 000 *[1 mark]*.
The salaries for company B are positively skewed, so there are more people with lower salaries and fewer people with higher salaries *[1 mark]*.

c) mean > median > mode *[1 mark]*

2 a) The runs scored by cricketer A are fairly uniform, so they were approximately equally likely to score any number of runs in the range *[1 mark]*.
The runs scored by cricketer B are negatively skewed, so they scored a higher number of runs more often *[1 mark]*.

b) Cricketer B — e.g. more of cricketer B's data is towards the higher end of the distribution
[1 mark for any sensible reason].

Page 36: Scatter Diagrams

1 a) 5 *[1 mark]*

b) E.g.

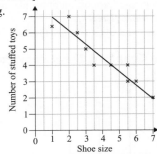

[1 mark for a suitable line of best fit drawn]
Your line of best fit might be slightly different but should have roughly the same number of points either side of the line.

c) There is negative correlation between shoe size and the number of stuffed toys owned *[1 mark]*.

2 a) The data is bivariate (has two variables) so a scatter diagram is appropriate as you can put one variable on each axis *[1 mark]*.

b) and c)

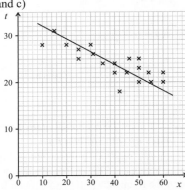

[2 marks available for b) — 2 marks for all points plotted correctly, otherwise 1 mark for at least 10 points plotted correctly]
[1 mark available for c) — 1 mark for a suitable line of best fit drawn]

d) There is negative correlation between patient age and the number of teeth with no fillings *[1 mark]*. This suggests that the older people are, the more fillings they're likely to have *[1 mark]*.

Page 37: Time Series Graphs

1 a)

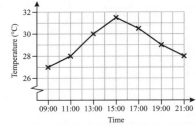

[2 marks available — 1 mark for all points plotted correctly, 1 mark for points joined by straight lines]

b) The graph has an upward trend until 15:00 hours and then it has a downward trend until 21:00 *[1 mark]*.

2 a)

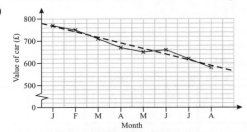

[3 marks available — 1 mark for all points plotted correctly, 1 mark for points joined by straight lines, 1 mark for a suitable trend line drawn]

Answers

b) The graph shows a downward trend *[1 mark]*.

c) Extend your trend line from part a) and read off the value for September — this is approximately £560.
[1 mark for any answer between £540 and £580]

Page 38: Choosing How to Represent Data

1 Method 1 — e.g. it shows the exact number of customers.
Method 2 — e.g. it shows proportions clearly.
Method 3 — e.g. the data is measured at time intervals / it shows the trend of the data clearly.
[3 marks available — 1 mark for a sensible and different reason for each method]

2 a) (i) E.g. Distance is continuous and stem and leaf diagrams show discrete data. / There are lots of data values, so it would take a long time to draw the diagram *[1 mark]*.

(ii) E.g. Distance is continuous and cumulative frequency diagrams show continuous data. / There are enough data values for grouping to be appropriate *[1 mark]*.

b) E.g. A histogram is probably not appropriate for his target audience, because the Year 7 students might have difficulty understanding the histogram *[1 mark]*.

Page 39: Misleading Diagrams

1 Any three from:
E.g. The symbols are different shapes, but represent the same number of students. / The symbols aren't lined up. / The building symbols are different sizes (the smaller one might represent fewer students). / The key doesn't specify whether the plain and shaded building symbols are worth the same. / There's no title. / It's hard to divide the sandwich symbol into two.
[1 mark for each sensible answer up to 3 marks]

2 E.g. The horizontal axis is angled downwards, which exaggerates the increasing trend of the line *[1 mark]*. The vertical axis is broken, which makes the rise in the line seem steeper *[1 mark]*.

3 E.g. The owner should choose pie chart 2 *[1 mark]* because Sector A has been shaded to stand out more and the 3D effect/volume makes it take up more area than it should do *[1 mark]*.
On pie charts 1 and 3, sector A takes up half the area of the pie chart, whereas on pie chart 2 it takes up more than half. You could argue that she should choose pie chart 1 as it's not misleading but still shows that her restaurant makes the most profit.

Section Four — Analysing and Interpreting Data

Pages 40-41: Mean, Median and Mode

1 a) Sum of numbers $= \overline{x} \times n = 5 \times 12 = 60$ *[1 mark]*
Sum of known numbers $= 50$
So sum of missing numbers $= 60 - 50 = 10$
For 7 to be the mode, one of the missing numbers must be 7 *[1 mark]*, so the other must be $10 - 7 = 3$ *[1 mark]*.

b) List the numbers in ascending order:
1, 2, 2, 3, 3, 5, 6, 7, 7, 7, 8, 9
Position of median $= (12 + 1) \div 2 = 6.5$
So the median is between 5 and 6, i.e. 5.5.
[2 marks available — 1 mark for ordering the numbers or using $(n + 1) \div 2$, 1 mark for the correct answer]

2 a) (i) The median *[1 mark]* since there is an outlier in the data *[1 mark for a sensible reason]*.

(ii) List the numbers in ascending order:
90, 2010, 2010, 2550, 2550, 2620, 2800, 3090
Position of median $= (8 + 1) \div 2 = 4.5$
So the median is between 2550 and 2550, i.e. 2550 hours.
[2 marks available — 1 mark for ordering the numbers or using $(n + 1) \div 2$, 1 mark for the correct answer]
If you got part (i) wrong and said that the mean was the best average, you'd still get the marks in part (ii) for correctly working out that the mean is 2215 hours.

b) (i) The mean lifetime would increase. *[1 mark]*

(ii) The median lifetime would stay the same. *[1 mark]*
Adding a larger value <u>sometimes</u> increases the median, but not always. In this case, it moves the median to the 5th position but the number in the 5th position is still 2550.

3 a) E.g. multiply each value by 10 000 and then subtract 300:
65, 21, 64, 83, 1, 12, 63, 1, 57, 29
Mean $= (65 + 21 + 64 + 83 + 1 + 12 + 63 + 1 + 57 + 29) \div 10$
$= 39.6$
Reverse the transformation to find the mean of the times:
$(39.6 + 300) \div 10\,000 = 0.03396$ minutes
[3 marks available — 1 mark for any correct linear transformation, 1 mark for a correct method to find the mean of the transformed values, 1 mark for the correct final answer]

b) Any one from:
The data is continuous. / The mode only exists by chance. / The mode only exists to the degree of accuracy given (i.e. in reality, there is no mode). / The mode would be 0.039, which is far away from the mean. *[1 mark for a suitable answer]*

4 Red dress weighted mean $= (40 \times 0.3) + (30 \times 0.5) + (60 \times 0.2)$
$= 39$
Blue dress weighted mean $= (45 \times 0.3) + (35 \times 0.5) + (20 \times 0.2)$
$= 35$
Jo should buy the red dress since it has the greater weighted mean.
[3 marks available — 1 mark for a correct method to find a weighted mean, 1 mark for both weighted means correct, 1 mark for the correct conclusion]

5 First building society: $\sqrt{1.04 \times 1.09} = 1.06470... = 6.47\%$ (2 d.p.)
The second building society has a fixed rate of 6.6%, which is greater than 6.47%, so the second building society gives the better overall rate.
[3 marks available — 1 mark for a correct method to find a geometric mean, 1 mark for the correct geometric mean, 1 mark for the correct conclusion]

Page 42: Averages from Frequency Tables

1 a) 100 *[1 mark]*

b) Number of bags $= 2 + 4 + 23 + ... + 6 + 5 = 300$
Position of median $= (300 + 1) \div 2 = 150.5$ *[1 mark]*
There are $2 + 4 + 23 + 53 = 82$ bags in the first four columns and $82 + 108 = 190$ bags in the first five columns. So the 150.5 position is in the fifth column. So the median number of nails per bag is 100 *[1 mark]*.

c) $\overline{x} = \dfrac{\sum fx}{\sum f} = \dfrac{(96 \times 2) + (97 \times 4) + ... + (103 \times 6) + (104 \times 5)}{2 + 4 + ... + 6 + 5}$
$= \dfrac{30\,045}{300}$ *[1 mark]* $= 100.15$ *[1 mark]*

2 a) (i) $p < 24$ (or $p \leq 23$) *[1 mark]*

(ii) Sum of known values $= 119$
So $p = 120 - 119 = 1$ *[1 mark]*

b) $\overline{x} = \dfrac{1128}{120}$ *[1 mark]* $= 9.4$ *[1 mark]*

c) The mean would increase. *[1 mark]*

Page 43: Averages from Grouped Data

1 a) $\overline{x} = \dfrac{(5 \times 22) + (15 \times 32) + (25 \times 45) + (35 \times 18) + (45 \times 3)}{22 + 32 + 45 + 18 + 3}$
$= \dfrac{2480}{120} = 20.66... = 20.7$ mins
[3 marks available — 1 mark for multiplying frequencies by the class midpoints, 1 mark for dividing $\sum fx$ by $\sum f$, 1 mark for the correct answer]

b) The data is grouped so you don't know the actual data values, which means you can only estimate the mean. *[1 mark]*

c) $20 \leq t < 30$ *[1 mark]*

d) Position of median = 120 ÷ 2 = 60
There are 22 + 32 = 54 values in the first two columns
and 54 + 45 = 99 values in the first three columns so
the median is in the 20 ≤ t < 30 class. *[1 mark]*
The median is the 60 − 54 = 6th value in the
class, out of 45 values. So it is 6 ÷ 45 = 0.133...
of the way through the group. *[1 mark]*
The class width is 10 so the median value is
20 + (10 × 0.133...) = 21.33... = 21.3 mins. *[1 mark]*

2 a) $\sum f = 2 + 15 + 24 + 24 + 18 + 8 = 91$
Position of median = 91 ÷ 2 = 45.5
There are 2 + 15 + 24 = 41 values in the first three columns
and 41 + 24 = 65 values in the first four columns so the
median is in the 110-119 group. *[1 mark]*

b) The midpoints are 50, 85, 105, 115, 135 and 170.
$\sum fx = (2 \times 50) + (15 \times 85) + (24 \times 105) + (24 \times 115)$
$+ (18 \times 135) + (8 \times 170)$
$= 10\,445$
$\overline{x} = \frac{10\,445}{91} = 114.78... = 115$ (3 s.f.)
*[3 marks available — 1 mark for multiplying frequencies
by the class midpoints, 1 mark for dividing $\sum fx$ by $\sum f$,
1 mark for the correct answer]*

Pages 44-45: Measures of Spread

1 a) Position of upper quartile = 3(31 + 1) ÷ 4 = 24
So Q_3 = 840 *[1 mark]*

b) Position of lower quartile = (31 + 1) ÷ 4 = 8
So Q_1 = 510 *[1 mark]*
*The values are in descending order so you need to either reorder
them or count up from the bottom to find the quartiles.*

c) IQR = 840 − 510 = 330 *[1 mark]*

2 a) 258 − 231 = 27 g *[1 mark]*

b) List the weights in ascending order:
231, 232, 233, 239, 242, 245, 245, 245, 246, 247, 250, 258
Position of Q_1 = (12 + 1) ÷ 4 = 3.25. So Q_1 is a quarter
of the way between 233 and 239, i.e. Q_1 = 234.5.
Position of Q_3 = 3(12 + 1) ÷ 4 = 9.75. So Q_3 is three quarters
of the way between 246 and 247, i.e. Q_3 = 246.75.
IQR = 246.75 − 234.5 = 12.25 g
*[2 marks available — 1 mark for at least one correct
quartile, 1 mark for the correct final answer]*

c) IQR = 250 − 240 = 10 g *[1 mark]*
The new mangos have a lower interquartile range
so the weights of the second set of mangos are
more consistent / less varied *[1 mark]*.

3 a) Dr. Smith & Partners: IQR = 3.7 − 2.1 = 1.6 kg *[1 mark]*
Happy Tot Hospital: IQR = 3.4 − 2.4 = 1.0 kg *[1 mark]*
The Happy Tot Hospital has a lower interquartile
range *[1 mark]* so the birth weights are more consistent here
than at Dr. Smith & Partners *[1 mark]*.
*Alternatively, you could work out the range of both hospitals
(4.2 and 3.9 respectively) and you'd then reach the same
conclusion. But you'll only get the marks if you use the two
IQRs together or the two ranges together, not one of each.*

b) Since 2.1 is the lower quartile, 25% of the data is below this
value. 25% of 23 = 0.25 × 2.3 *[1 mark]*
= 5.75 so 6 babies *[1 mark]*

4 a) The interdecile range uses the middle 80% of the data, so 20%
is not included. 20% of 140 = 28 sunflowers *[1 mark]*

b) There are some very tall and/or very short
sunflowers (i.e. the greatest and/or lowest values
are far away from D_9/D_1) *[1 mark]*.

c) Yes, she is correct. D_9 ≤ greatest value and D_1 ≥ lowest value
so the difference can never be larger *[1 mark]*.

Page 46: Measures of Spread — Grouped Data

1 a) Reading across from 120 × 0.35 = 42:
P_{35} = 50 minutes *[1 mark]*

b) Reading across from 120 × 0.25 = 30: Q_1 = 44 minutes
Reading across from 120 × 0.75 = 90: Q_3 = 70 minutes
IQR = 70 − 44 = 26 minutes
*[2 marks available — 1 mark for at least one correct
quartile, 1 mark for the correct final answer]*

c) Reading across from 120 × 0.6 = 72: P_{60} = 62 minutes
Reading across from 120 × 0.8 = 96: P_{80} = 74 minutes
$P_{80} − P_{60}$ = 12 minutes
*[2 marks available — 1 mark for at least one correct
percentile, 1 mark for the correct final answer]*

d) The P_{60} to P_{80} interpercentile range is higher for the television
guide so there is less consistency in the times spent reading
the television guide in this upper 20% of the data *[1 mark]*.
The median newspaper time is found by reading across from
120 × 0.5 = 60 on the graph: median = 57 minutes *[1 mark]*
So people spent longer on average reading the newspaper than
reading the television guide *[1 mark]*.

Page 47: Standard Deviation

1 $\sigma = \sqrt{\frac{3840}{12} - \left(\frac{208.8}{12}\right)^2}$ *[1 mark]* = 4.152...
= 4.15 (2 d.p.) *[1 mark]*
*Remember, the formulas for the standard deviation will be on your
formula sheet.*

2 a) $\overline{x} = \frac{\sum x}{n} = \frac{429.3}{5} = 85.86$ kg *[1 mark]*

b) $\sum (x - \overline{x})^2 = (85.8 - 85.86)^2 + (85.9 - 85.86)^2$
$+ (86.0 - 85.86)^2 + (85.7 - 85.86)^2$
$+ (85.9 - 85.86)^2$ *[1 mark]*
= 0.052 *[1 mark]*

c) $\sigma = \sqrt{\frac{0.052}{5}} = 0.1019... = 0.102$ kg (3 s.f.) *[1 mark]*

3 a) $\sigma = \sqrt{\frac{\sum x^2}{10} - \left(\frac{\sum x}{10}\right)^2} = \sqrt{\frac{385}{10} - \left(\frac{55}{10}\right)^2} = 2.8722...$
= 2.87 (3 s.f.)
*[2 marks available — 1 mark for substituting correctly
into a formula for the standard deviation, 1 mark for
the correct answer]*
You could have used the formula involving $\sum(x - \overline{x})^2$ instead.

b) The standard deviation of these numbers is also
2.8722... since the values are dispersed in exactly the
same way (i.e. there are 10 values and the difference
between each consecutive value is 1) *[1 mark]*.

Page 48: Standard Deviation from Frequency Tables

1 a) $\sigma = \sqrt{\frac{258}{25} - \left(\frac{70}{25}\right)^2}$ *[1 mark]* = 1.5748...
= 1.6 (2 s.f.) *[1 mark]*

b) The mean for the first group is 70 ÷ 25 = 2.8 crabs *[1 mark]*.
This is less than the mean for the second group so the second
group caught more crabs on average *[1 mark]*.
The standard deviation for the second group was lower so the
numbers of crabs caught by this group were generally closer
to the mean than those caught by the first group *[1 mark]*.

2 a) $\sum ft = (7.5 \times 1) + (17.5 \times 8) + (22.5 \times 12)$
$+ (27.5 \times 8) + (32.5 \times 1) = 670$
$\sigma = \sqrt{\frac{15687.5}{30} - \left(\frac{670}{30}\right)^2} = 4.913... = 4.9$ seconds (1 d.p.)
*[2 marks available — 1 mark for multiplying frequencies by
the class midpoints to find $\sum ft$, 1 mark for using the correct
formula to reach the given answer]*

b) The data is grouped so you don't know the actual times,
meaning you can only estimate the standard deviation *[1 mark]*.
*This method uses an estimate of 7.5 secs for the fastest time (the
midpoint of the group O < t ≤ 15), but this is probably much too
low. The real value in the group is likely to be greater than 11 secs.*

Page 49: Box Plots

1 Lowest value = 0, Q_1 = 12, Median = 26,
   Q_3 = 38, greatest value = 76

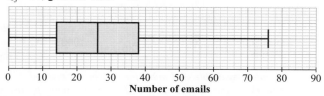

*[3 marks available — 1 mark for a correctly drawn median line,
1 mark for a correctly drawn box showing quartiles,
1 mark for correctly drawn whiskers]*

2 a) Median for Abbeyknock = 60% *[1 mark]*
   b) Q_1 = 55 and Q_3 = 80, so IQR = 80 − 55 *[1 mark]*
                                = 25% *[1 mark]*
   c) The median for Blakeney is greater than that of Abbeyknock,
       so the students of Blakeney did better on average.
       The (interquartile) range is smaller for Blakeney than for
       Abbeyknock, so the results were more consistent at Blakeney.
       There is a negative skew at Blakeney, meaning more
       pupils had higher marks, but the distribution is much more
       symmetrical at Abbeyknock.
       *[4 marks available — 1 mark for comparing the medians,
       1 mark for comparing the (interquartile) ranges, 1 mark for
       comparing the skews, 1 mark for a contextual interpretation]*

Page 50: Outliers

1 a) 114 g *[1 mark]*
   b) IQR = 106 − 102 = 4 g *[1 mark]*
       Q_3 + 1.5 × IQR = 106 + 1.5 × 4 = 112 g *[1 mark]*
       Since 114 g > 112 g, it is an outlier. *[1 mark]*
       *If you thought there was a low outlier, you'd do
       Q_1 − 1.5 × IQR = 96 g. All the values are greater
       than this, so there aren't any low outliers.*
   c)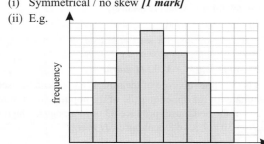
       [1 mark]
2 a) $\sum c = 686$ *[1 mark]*
       $\bar{c} = 686 \div 20 = 34.3$ *[1 mark]*
   b) $\sigma = \sqrt{\dfrac{1512.2}{20}} = 8.6954... = 8.70$ (2 d.p.) *[1 mark]*
   c) Outliers are outside the interval
       $\bar{c} \pm 3\sigma = (8.21..., 60.38...)$ *[1 mark]*
       All of the data is within this interval,
       so there are no outliers. *[1 mark]*

Page 51: Skewness of Data

1 a) (i) Symmetrical / no skew *[1 mark]*
       (ii) E.g.

   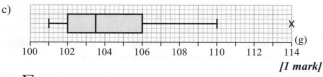

   [1 mark for a roughly symmetrical histogram]
   b) (i) Positive *[1 mark]*

   (ii) E.g.

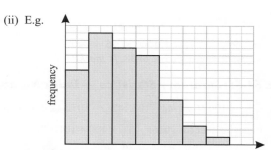

*[1 mark for a histogram with the peak on the left
and a descending tail on the right]*

2 a) Median > mean, implying negative skew
       *[2 marks available — 1 mark for an inequality involving the
       mean and median, 1 mark for the correct prediction]*
   b) $\dfrac{3(8-9)}{1.2}$ *[1 mark]* = −2.5 *[1 mark]*
   c) The value is negative, so the skew is negative. This suggests
       the majority of the scores were relatively high (or the scores
       were more consistent / densely distributed above the median).
       [1 mark for a sensible answer]

Page 52: Comparing Data Sets

1 E.g. The median for the men is greater, suggesting the men
   travelled further on average. The (interquartile) range is greater
   for women, suggesting the distanced travelled by the women
   is less consistent. The distances travelled by the women has a
   positive skew, whereas those travelled by the men have a slightly
   negative skew. This means the women's distances were more
   densely distributed below their median of 14 miles and the men's
   were more densely distributed above their median of 24 miles.
   *[4 marks available — 1 mark for correctly comparing medians,
   1 mark for correctly comparing (interquartile) ranges, 1 mark for
   correctly identifying women's skew, 1 mark for correctly
   identifying men's skew]*
2 a) The claim seems reasonable *[1 mark]*
       since Batsman A's interquartile range is lower *[1 mark]*.
   b) E.g. No, the statement is not valid. *[1 mark]*
       The statement is based on Batsman A having the higher
       mean and lower interquartile range, but the mean should
       not be paired with the interquartile range. *[1 mark]*
       *Or you could say that the median (which can be
       paired with the interquartile range) of Batsman B
       is higher, suggesting he is the better batsman.*

Page 53: Standardised Scores

1 a) $\dfrac{32-30}{4.6}$ *[1 mark]* = 0.4347... = 0.435 (3 s.f.) *[1 mark]*
   b) $0.343 = \dfrac{time - 25}{6.7}$ *[1 mark]*
       $\Rightarrow$ time = (0.343 × 6.7) + 25 = 27.29...
                                        = 27.3 seconds (3 s.f.) *[1 mark]*
2 a) (i) Compulsory: $\dfrac{40-37.25}{5.07} = 0.542...$
            Freestyle: $\dfrac{44-41.7}{3.2} = 0.718...$
            Total standardised score = 0.542... + 0.718...
                                     = 1.261... = 1.26 (3 s.f.)
            *[3 marks available — 1 mark for a correct method to
            find a score, 1 mark for both correct scores, 1 mark for
            the correct final answer]*
       (ii) Nathan's total standardised score
            $= \dfrac{43-37.25}{5.07} + \dfrac{41-41.7}{3.2} = 0.9153... = 0.915$ (3 s.f.)
            Zac's total standardised score is higher, so Zac gave the
            better overall performance.
            *[3 marks available — 1 mark for a correct method
            to find Nathan's standardised score, 1 mark for
            Nathan's correct standardised score, 1 mark for
            the correct conclusion linked to an explanation]*

b) $0.15 = \dfrac{\text{score} - 37.25}{5.07}$ *[1 mark]*

$\Rightarrow$ score = $(0.15 \times 5.07) + 37.25 = 38.0105$
So she received a score of 38. *[1 mark]*

Pages 54-55: Summary Statistics — Index Numbers

1 a) $\dfrac{450}{420} \times 100$ *[1 mark]* = 107.142... = 107.1 (1 d.p.) *[1 mark]*

b) Index number for 2016: $\dfrac{425}{420} \times 100 = 101.190...$ ($\approx 1.19\%$)

Index number for 2017: $\dfrac{430}{420} \times 100 = 102.380...$ ($\approx 2.38\%$)

From 2015 to 2016, the increase in price was greater than the increase in CPI (1.19% > 0.7%).
From 2015 to 2017, the increase in price was less than the increase in CPI (2.38% < 2.7%).
[5 marks available — 1 mark for a correct method to find an index number for 2016 or 2017, 1 mark for the correct 2016 index number, 1 mark for the correct 2017 index number, 1 mark for the correct 2016 conclusion, 1 mark for the correct 2017 conclusion]

2 Milk index × weight = $\left(\dfrac{1.20}{1.00} \times 100\right) \times 58 = 6960$

Bananas index × weight = $\left(\dfrac{0.52}{0.44} \times 100\right) \times 25 = 2954.5...$

Strawberries index × weight = $\left(\dfrac{0.38}{0.30} \times 100\right) \times 17 = 2153.3...$

Weighted index number = $\dfrac{6960 + 2954.5... + 2153.3...}{58 + 25 + 17}$
$= 120.67... = 120.7$ (4 s.f.)

[4 marks available — 1 mark for the correct formula for one of the ingredients, 1 mark for all three values correct, 1 mark for the correct formula for the weighted index number, 1 mark for the correct final answer]

3 a) 2 *[1 mark]*

b) Steel A index × weight = $\left(\dfrac{280}{275} \times 100\right) \times 3 = 305.45...$

Steel B index × weight = $\left(\dfrac{305}{275} \times 100\right) \times 2 = 221.81...$

Weighted index number = $\dfrac{305.45... + 221.81...}{3 + 2}$
$= 105.45... = 105.5$ (1 d.p.)
[4 marks available — 1 mark for the correct formula for one of the types of steel, 1 mark for both steel values correct, 1 mark for the correct formula for the weighted index number, 1 mark for the correct final answer]

c) 5.5% (1 d.p.) *[1 mark]*

4 a) 2015: $\dfrac{483}{471} \times 100 = 102.547... = 102.55$ (2 d.p.)

2016: $\dfrac{495}{483} \times 100 = 102.484... = 102.48$ (2 d.p.)

2017: $\dfrac{506}{495} \times 100 = 102.222... = 102.22$ (2 d.p.)

[3 marks available — 1 mark for one correct formula, 1 mark for a second correct formula, 1 mark for all three index numbers correct]

b) Earnings increased by 2.55% between 2014 and 2015. *[1 mark]*
Earnings increased by 2.48% between 2015 and 2016. *[1 mark]*
Earnings increased by 2.22% between 2016 and 2017. *[1 mark]*

Pages 56-57: Summary Statistics — Rates of Change

1 a) Crude birth rate for Wentwell = $\dfrac{432}{28\,600} \times 1000$
$= 15.10... = 15.1$ (1 d.p.)

Number of births in Bourneland = $\dfrac{21.4 \times 15\,000}{1000} = 321$

[3 marks available — 1 mark for the correct method to find one of the missing numbers, 1 mark for the correct crude birth rate of Wentwell, 1 mark for the correct number of births in Bourneland]

b) $15.10... \div 10 = 1.51$ births (2 d.p.) *[1 mark]*
Alternatively, you might have done $\dfrac{432}{28600} \times 100 = 1.51$ (2 d.p.).

2 a) Mudgrave: $\dfrac{120 + 320 + 5260}{57\,000 + 30\,000 + 44\,000} \times 1000 = 43.51...$
$= 43.5$ (1 d.p.)

Ollington: $\dfrac{100 + 500 + 8050}{80\,000 + 49\,000 + 86\,000} \times 1000 = 40.23...$
$= 40.2$ (1 d.p.)

[3 marks available — 1 mark for the correct method, 1 mark for the correct rate for Mudgrave, 1 mark for the correct rate for Ollington]

b) Ollington *[1 mark]*

c) They will take into account the differences in the age distributions *[1 mark]*, e.g. Ollington has a higher proportion of older people so this might increase the crude death rate *[1 mark for a sensible comment]*.

3 a) Hadham, since it has a higher percentage of people of childbearing age. *[1 mark for a sensible reason]*

b) The standardised rate is likely to be lower as it will take the high percentage of people of childbearing age into account. *[1 mark]*

4 a) $\dfrac{4213 + 78\,038 + 402\,116}{63\,182\,000} \times 1000$ *[1 mark]*
$= 7.6662... = 7.67$ (3 s.f.) *[1 mark]*

b) 0-14: $\dfrac{11.1}{63.182} \times 1000 = 175.68...$ *[1 mark]*

15-64: $\dfrac{41.706}{63.182} \times 1000 = 660.09...$ *[1 mark]*

65 or older: $\dfrac{10.376}{63.182} \times 1000 = 164.22...$ *[1 mark]*

c) 0-14: $\dfrac{4213}{63\,182\,000} \times 175.68... = 0.0117...$

15-64: $\dfrac{78\,038}{63\,182\,000} \times 660.09 = 0.8153...$

65 or older: $\dfrac{402\,116}{63\,182\,000} \times 164.25... = 1.045...$

$0.0117... + 0.8153... + 1.045... = 1.872... = 1.9$ (1 d.p.)
[3 marks available — 1 mark for the correct method for the standardised rate for the age groups, 1 mark for at least one correct standardised rate, 1 mark for adding the rates together to reach the given answer]

Page 58: Estimating Population Characteristics

1 a) Mean of sample = $122.5 \div 10 = 12.25$ cm *[1 mark]*
So estimate for the mean of population = 12.25 cm *[1 mark]*

b) Any one from:
10 slugs is unlikely to be a large enough sample. / It is difficult to accurately measure a slug. / Samar may have made an error in her measurements. / The sample may not be representative.
[1 mark for any sensible answer]

c) E.g. Slugs live in lots of different places, not just gardens, so the garden is unlikely to be representative of the UK.
[1 mark for any sensible answer]

2 a) $240 \div 6 = 40$ *[1 mark]*
You might have used the median instead of the mean. On this occasion, the answer is the same.

b) 30×40 *[1 mark]* = 1200 *[1 mark]*

c) 43 is the upper quartile of the sample and so can be used as an estimate for the upper quartile of the population. *[1 mark]*
25% of the henhouses produce 43 or more eggs, which is $0.25 \times 30 = 7.5$, so 8 henhouses. *[1 mark]*

Answers

Page 59: Estimating Population Sizes

1 a) Yes. E.g. people cannot enter or leave the ship / people on a cruise ship move about and mix back in. *[1 mark]*

b) No. The trees are fixed and so can't mix. *[1 mark]*

2 a) $\frac{10}{N} = \frac{2}{8}$ *[1 mark]* $\Rightarrow N = \frac{10 \times 8}{2} = 40$ *[1 mark]*

b) Any one from:
The population is constant (no mice are born, die, enter or leave the warehouse). / The mice are not affected by the tags. / The mice mix back in when they're released. / The samples are representative and random.
[1 mark for any sensible answer]

3 No, it is not an accurate conclusion. *[1 mark]*
E.g. Ten months is too long to assume the population remains constant. / The first sample is too small to represent the whole deer population. *[1 mark for a sensible comment]*

Section Five — Analysing and Interpreting Diagrams

Pages 60-61: Scatter Diagrams

1 a)

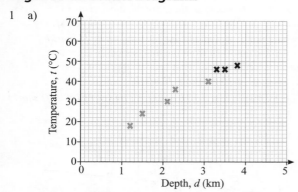

[1 mark for all three correct]

b) There is (strong) positive correlation *[1 mark]*. This means that as the depth below the seabed increases, the temperature also increases. *[1 mark]*

c) (i) $(18 + 24 + 30 + 36 + 40 + 46 + 46 + 48) \div 8$ *[1 mark]*
= $288 \div 8 = 36$ °C *[1 mark]*

(ii) Draw the line of best fit through the double mean point (2.6, 36).

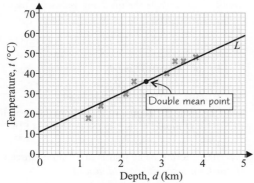

[1 mark for an appropriate straight line drawn through the double mean point]
Your line might not be in exactly the same place but it should have roughly the same number of points on either side and cover at least the interval from d = 1 to d = 4.

d) (i) 30 °C *[1 mark]*
Allow 27 °C to 33 °C based on your line of best fit.

(ii) Seabed at d = 0 km. Temperature here is 11 °C *[1 mark]*.
Allow 8 °C to 14 °C based on your line of best fit.
The answer is unreliable since it involves extrapolating / 0 km is outside the range of the known data. *[1 mark]*

e) (i) Find two points on the line.
E.g. when $d = 1$, $t = -6 + 16 \times 1 = 10$ and when $d = 2$, $t = -6 + 16 \times 2 = 26$.
So (1, 10) and (2, 26) are on the line.
Then draw the regression line through these points.

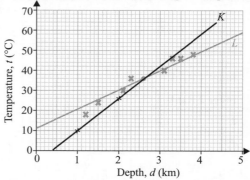

[2 marks available — 1 mark for calculating two points on the line, 1 mark for the correctly drawn regression line]

(ii) The gradient is the change in temperature as depth increases *[1 mark]*. According to this line, the temperature increases by 16 °C for every 1 km increase in depth *[1 mark]*.

2 a)

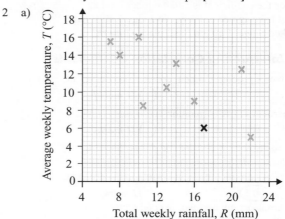

[1 mark]

b) (i) The diagram does support the claim *[1 mark]* since there is a negative correlation (i.e. as rainfall increases, temperature decreases) *[1 mark]*.

(ii) The forecaster isn't necessarily justified since temperature and rainfall being correlated does not mean that a change in one causes a change in the other. *[1 mark for commenting in context that correlation does not imply causation]*

c) $b = \frac{12 - 9}{11 - 19} = -\frac{3}{8} = -0.375$
Substituting (11, 12) into the equation:
$12 = a - 0.375 \times 11 \Rightarrow a = 16.125$
So the equation is $T = 16.125 - 0.375R$
[2 marks available — 1 mark for the correct value of a, 1 mark for the correct value of b]

d) $T = 16.125 - 0.375 \times 18$ *[1 mark]*
= 9.375 = 9.4 °C (1 d.p.) *[1 mark]*

e) Either:
It would be appropriate since this is interpolating / 17 mm is within the range of the known data.
Or:
It would be inappropriate since the correlation doesn't look very strong. *[1 mark for a sensible explanation]*

Page 62: Spearman's Rank Correlation Coefficient

1 a) Weak negative correlation *[1 mark]*

 b) There is little to no link between how well people did in karting and how well they did in skiing. *[1 mark]*

2 a)

Singer	A	B	C	D	E	F	G	H
Judge 1	8	6	10	9	5	7	4	3
Judge 2	6	7	9	10	5	3	4	8
Judge 1 Rank	3	5	1	2	6	4	7	8
Judge 2 Rank	5	4	2	1	6	8	7	3
d	−2	1	−1	1	0	−4	0	5
d^2	4	1	1	1	0	16	0	25

$$r_s = 1 - \frac{6(4+1+1+1+0+16+0+25)}{8(8^2-1)}$$
$$= 1 - \frac{288}{504} = 0.428... = 0.43 \text{ (2 d.p.)}$$

[4 marks available — 1 mark for ranking both judges' scores, 1 mark for correct differences in ranks, 1 mark for using the correct formula, 1 mark for the correct answer]

 b) There is (moderate) positive (rank) correlation *[1 mark]*, so there was some agreement between the judges *[1 mark]*.

 c) Since the coefficient is 1.0, the judges' ranks must have agreed entirely. So Judge 3 must have ranked Singer F in 8th (last) place *[1 mark]*.

Page 63: Interpreting Correlation Coefficients

1 a) Pearson's product moment correlation coefficient:

 −1   −0.5   0   0.5   ① *[1 mark]*

 Spearman's rank correlation coefficient:

 −1   −0.5   0   0.5   ① *[1 mark]*

 The points lie on a straight line sloping upwards, so this is perfect positive linear correlation.

 b) Pearson's product moment correlation coefficient:

 −1   ⊖0.5   0   0.5   1 *[1 mark]*

 Spearman's rank correlation coefficient:

 ⊖1   −0.5   0   0.5   1 *[1 mark]*

 Each time the x-variable increases, the y-variable decreases so there is a perfect negative association. But the points don't lie close to a straight line so it isn't linear, meaning the PMCC will be closer to O than the SRCC.

2 a) There is some positive correlation between the marks awarded by the two friends. *[1 mark]*

 b) (i) E.g. 0.8 *[1 mark]*
 Any value strictly greater than O.5 but strictly less than 1 would get you the mark.

 (ii) The ranks of the scores are clearly similar but they don't lie on a straight line *[1 mark]*, so Pearson's product moment correlation coefficient will be less than Spearman's rank correlation coefficient. *[1 mark]*

Pages 64-65: Time Series

1 a) $(690 + 770 + 820 + 860) \div 4 = 785$
 $(770 + 820 + 860 + 680) \div 4 = 782.5$
 [3 marks available — 1 mark for the correct method to find one of the moving averages, 1 mark for each correct moving average]

b)

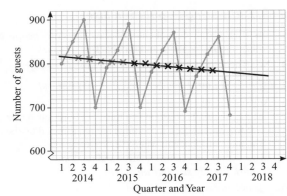

[3 marks available — 2 marks for all eight moving averages plotted correctly, otherwise 1 mark for four to seven moving averages plotted correctly, 1 mark for a trend line passing through/close to all the moving averages]

 c) Quarter 4 *[1 mark]*

 d) The trend is downwards *[1 mark]*, so the number of guests is decreasing over time *[1 mark]*.

 e) The seasonal variation is highest in Quarter 3 and lowest in Quarter 4 *[1 mark]* so there are the most visits in Quarter 3 and the fewest visits in Quarter 4 *[1 mark]*.

 f) It would not be suitable to use the time series *[1 mark]* since you cannot tell from the time series when the trend started/what happened prior to 2014 (i.e. it's extrapolating) *[1 mark]*.

2 a) $(21.0 + 16.3 + 14.9) \div 3$ *[1 mark]* $= 17.4$ (or £17 400) *[1 mark]*

b)

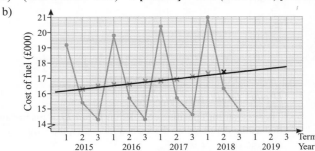

[2 marks available — 1 mark for the remaining moving average plotted correctly, 1 mark for a trend line passing through/close to all the moving averages]

 c) $15.7 - 16.7 = -1.0$ (or −£1000) *[1 mark]*
 Since 16.7 comes from the trend line, your value might be slightly different depending on how you've drawn your line.

 d) $\frac{(15.4 - 16.3) + (15.7 - 16.7) + (15.7 - 17) + (16.3 - 17.3)}{4}$ *[1 mark]*
 $= -1.05$ (or −£1050) *[1 mark]*
 16.3, 16.7, 17 and 17.3 are all from the trend line so your answer might be slightly different.

 e) Read the value for Term 2 of 2019 from the trend line: 17.6
 $17.6 - 1.4$ *[1 mark]* $= 16.2$ so the estimate is £16 200 *[1 mark]*

 f) The pattern in the school's fuel bills repeats every three terms. / The year is divided into three terms.
 [1 mark for a sensible explanation]

Section Six — Probability

Page 66: Probability

1 a)-c)

 [1 mark for the correct position of a), 1 mark for the correct position of b), 1 mark for the correct position of c)]

2 $3 + 6 = 9$ marbles are not silver, and there are 10 marbles in total,
so P(not silver) $= \frac{9}{10}$ *[1 mark]*.
Alternatively, you could have done $1 - P(silver)$ here.

3 a) There is 1 ticket numbered 16, out of 20 in total,
so P(16) $= \frac{1}{20} = 0.05 = 5\%$ *[1 mark]*.

   b) The primes between 1 and 20 are 2, 3, 5, 7, 11, 13, 17 and 19
[1 mark]. There are 8 primes *[1 mark]* out of 20 in total,
so P(prime) $= \frac{8}{20} = 0.4$ *[1 mark]*.

4 There are four possible outcomes (A, B, C and D) and the
probabilities of all possible outcomes add up to 1.
So P(A) + P(B) + P(C) + P(D) = 1
$\Rightarrow$ P(D) = 1 – P(A) – P(B) – P(C)
$= 1 - \frac{3}{10} - \frac{1}{5} - \frac{3}{20} = \frac{7}{20}$
*[2 marks available — 1 mark for using the fact that the sum of
probabilities of all possible outcomes is 1, 1 mark for the correct
answer]*

Page 67: Relative Frequency and Risk

1 a) Relative frequency of spinning a '1'
$= \frac{\text{number of times 1 was spun}}{\text{number of spins}} = \frac{14}{50} = 0.28$ *[1 mark]*
*You could have given your answer as a fraction here, but a
decimal is useful as it makes it easier to answer part b).*

   b) On a fair spinner, the probability of spinning a '1' is
$\frac{1}{6} = 0.166...$, but the relative frequency is 0.28. This is much
higher, which could suggest that the spinner is biased.
*[2 marks available — 1 mark for calculating the probability
for a fair spinner, 1 mark for comparing it to the relative
frequency and drawing a conclusion]*

2 Number of observations $= 16 + 80 = 96$ *[1 mark]*
Relative frequency of seeing a natterjack toad
$= \frac{\text{number of times she saw a natterjack toad}}{\text{number of observations}} = \frac{16}{96} = \frac{1}{6}$ *[1 mark]*

3 a) Absolute risk $= \frac{\text{number of boys who have broken a bone}}{\text{number of boys}}$
$= \frac{48}{100} = 0.48$ *[1 mark]*
Remember — absolute risk is the same as relative frequency.

   b) Absolute risk for girls $= \frac{9}{150} = 0.06$
Relative risk $= \frac{\text{absolute risk for boys}}{\text{absolute risk for girls}} = \frac{0.48}{0.06} = 8$,
so the boys are 8 times more likely to have broken a bone
than the girls.
*[3 marks available — 1 mark for the correct absolute risk for
the girls, 1 mark for dividing the absolute risk for the boys by
the absolute risk for the girls, 1 mark for the correct answer
interpreted in context]*

Page 68: Expected and Actual Frequencies

1 a) Expected frequency = number of penguins × probability
$= 280 \times 0.05 = 14$ misshapen penguins *[1 mark]*

   b) Probability of box passing quality check
$= 100\% - 10\% = 90\%$ *[1 mark]*
Number of boxes expected to pass quality check
= number of boxes × probability $= 120 \times 0.9 = 108$ *[1 mark]*

2 a)

Outcome	First	Second	Third or worse
Expected Frequency	$10 \times 0.7 = 7$	$10 \times 0.2 = 2$	$10 \times 0.1 = 1$

*[2 marks for all three entries correct, otherwise 1 mark for
two entries correct]*

b)

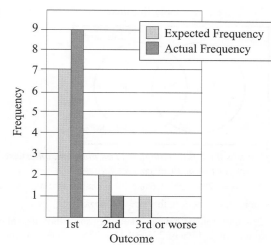

*[2 marks available — 1 mark for correct bars for expected
frequencies, 1 mark for correct bars for actual frequencies]*

c) E.g. Lucy could record the outcomes of more quizzes — 10 is
a very small sample size *[1 mark for a sensible explanation]*.

Page 69: Sample Space Diagrams

1 a) E.g.

		Spinner				
		1	2	3	4	5
Dice	1	2	3	4	5	6
	2	3	4	5	6	7
	3	4	5	6	7	8
	4	5	6	7	8	9
	5	6	7	8	9	10
	6	7	8	9	10	11

*[2 marks available — 2 marks for a fully correct sample
space diagram, otherwise 1 mark for setting up a suitable
diagram]*

   b) There are 6 outcomes that are 9 or more *[1 mark]*, out of a
total of $5 \times 6 = 30$ outcomes, so P(9 or more) $= \frac{6}{30} = \frac{1}{5}$
[1 mark].

2 a)

[1 mark]

   b) (i) There are 9 pairs of odd numbers out of 36 pairs,
so P(two odd numbers) $= \frac{9}{36} = \frac{1}{4}$ *[1 mark]*.

      (ii) There are 21 pairs that add up to less than 8 *[1 mark]*,
so P(total less than 8) $= \frac{21}{36} = \frac{7}{12}$ *[1 mark]*.

      (iii) There are 6 pairs that have a difference of 3 *[1 mark]*,
so P(difference of 3) $= \frac{6}{36} = \frac{1}{6}$ *[1 mark]*.

Pages 70-71: Venn Diagrams and Two-Way Tables

1 a) The intersection is people who have ketchup and mustard, so
this is 2%. 14% in total have ketchup, so $14\% - 2\% = 12\%$
goes in the rest of that circle. 8% of people in total have
mustard, so that leaves $8\% - 2\% = 6\%$ in the rest of that circle.
Everyone else has neither ketchup nor mustard, so
$100\% - 2\% - 12\% - 6\% = 80\%$ goes outside the circles.

The Venn diagram looks like this:

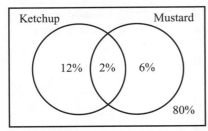

[2 marks for a fully complete Venn diagram, otherwise 1 mark for two or three correct values]

b) There is a 12% + 2% + 6% = 20% chance that a customer had sauce. As a fraction, this is $\frac{1}{5}$ *[1 mark]*.

c) 12% of customers have just ketchup, so the hot dog seller would expect 12% of 275 = 0.12 × 275 = 33 customers to have just ketchup.
[2 marks available — 1 mark for correctly identifying that 12% of customers have just ketchup, 1 mark for the correct answer]

2 a)

	Red	Blue	Green	White	Total
Car	12	12	32 − 12 − 12 − 3 = 5	3	32
Lorry	2	1	0	11	2 + 1 + 0 + 11 = 14
Motor-bike	4 − 2 − 0 − 1 = 1	2	0	1	4
Total	12 + 2 + 1 = 15	12 + 1 + 2 = 15	5 + 0 + 0 = 5	3 + 11 + 1 = 15	32 + 14 + 4 = 50

[3 marks available — 1 mark for correct values for both green cars and red motorbikes, 1 mark for correct column totals, 1 mark for correct row totals (including overall total)]

b) (i) There are 0 green motorbikes so P(green motorbike) = 0 *[1 mark]*.

(ii) There are 15 blue vehicles out of a total of 50, so P(blue) = $\frac{15}{50} = \frac{3}{10}$ (or 0.3 or 30%) *[1 mark]*.

3 a) There are several ways to calculate values for the table. E.g.
The male total is 40 − 15 = 25
30% of all employees are on foot: 30% of 40 = 0.3 × 40 = 12
Therefore total on moped = 40 − 20 − 12 = 8
$\frac{1}{3}$ of females use a car: $\frac{1}{3}$ of 15 = 5
So male car users = 20 − 5 = 15
$\frac{1}{3}$ of those on foot are male: $\frac{1}{3}$ of 12 = 4
So male moped = 25 − 4 − 15 = 6, female moped = 8 − 6 = 2, and female on foot = 12 − 4 = 8.
So the completed table looks like this:

	Car	Moped	Foot	Total
Male	15	6	4	25
Female	5	2	8	15
Total	20	8	12	40

[3 marks available — 1 mark for each correct row]

b) (i) There are 25 males out of 40 people in total, so P(male) = $\frac{25}{40} = \frac{5}{8}$ (or 0.625 or 62.5%) *[1 mark]*.

(ii) There are 8 females who deliver on foot so P(female who delivers on foot) = $\frac{8}{40} = \frac{1}{5}$ (or 0.2 or 20%) *[1 mark]*.

4 a) 1 person didn't like any of the biscuits, so this person would go outside all the circles, so x = 1 *[1 mark]*. 27 people were asked in total, so 1 + 3 + 9 + 6 + 3 + 1 + 2 + y = 27 ⟹ y = 2 *[1 mark]*.

b) 2 + 1 + 3 + 2 = 8 people like ginger biscuits *[1 mark]* out of a total of 27, so P(likes ginger biscuits) = $\frac{8}{27}$ *[1 mark]*.

c) 9 people like cookies and chocolate digestives but not ginger biscuits *[1 mark]*, so P(just cookies and chocolate digestives) = $\frac{9}{27} = \frac{1}{3}$ *[1 mark]*.

Page 72: The Addition Law

1 a) Yes, the events are mutually exclusive as no two of them can happen at the same time — e.g. a packet of crisps can't be both cheese & onion and salt & vinegar.
[2 marks available — 1 mark for stating that the events are mutually exclusive, 1 mark for a sensible explanation]

b) (i) There are 3 + 5 + 4 = 12 packets in total, and 5 of these are roast chicken, so P(roast chicken) = $\frac{5}{12}$ *[1 mark]*.

(ii) 3 + 4 = 7 packets are cheese & onion or salt & vinegar, so P(cheese & onion or salt & vinegar) = $\frac{7}{12}$ *[1 mark]*.
There are a couple of different ways you could have done this question — 'cheese & onion or salt & vinegar' is the same as 'not roast chicken', so you could have subtracted the probability you found in part (i) from 1. Or, you could have worked out P(cheese & onion) and P(salt & vinegar) separately and added them together (this is the addition law).

2 a) No, events A and B are not mutually exclusive as P(A and B) is not 0.
[2 marks available — 1 mark for stating that the events are not mutually exclusive, 1 mark for a sensible explanation]

b) Using the general addition law,
P(A or B) = P(A) + P(B) − P(A and B)
= 0.45 + 0.35 − 0.08 *[1 mark]* = 0.72 *[1 mark]*

3 P(jack) = $\frac{4}{52}$, P(spade) = $\frac{13}{52}$ and P(jack of spades) = $\frac{1}{52}$
So P(jack or spade) = P(jack) + P(spade) − P(jack and spade)
= $\frac{4}{52} + \frac{13}{52} - \frac{1}{52} = \frac{16}{52} = \frac{4}{13}$
[3 marks available — 1 mark for the correct individual probabilities, 1 mark for using the general addition formula, 1 mark for the correct answer]

Page 73: Independent Events

1 a) Yes, the events are independent, as
P(K) × P(D) = 0.6 × 0.3 = 0.18, which is the same as P(K and D) — if the events were not independent, these probabilities would not be the same.
[2 marks available — 1 mark for stating that the events are independent, 1 mark for explaining why]

b) P(only Katie goes) = 0.6 − 0.18 = 0.42
P(only Daniel goes) = 0.3 − 0.18 = 0.12
So P(only one goes) = 0.42 + 0.12 = 0.54
[2 marks available — 1 mark for a correct method, 1 mark for the correct answer]
You can use a Venn diagram to work out the separate probabilities if you need to. Or, you could have worked out P(only K) by doing 0.6 × (1 − 0.3) — this is P(K and not D), and similarly for P(only D), then add the resulting probabilities. The events are independent so it's OK to multiply P(K) by P(not D), and P(not K) by P(D).

2 It's easier to work out the probability of Ore not leaving any cakes in the oven too long and then subtract it from 1.
P(Ore doesn't leave a cake in the oven too long) = 1 − 0.15 = 0.85 *[1 mark]*
So P(Ore doesn't leave any cakes in the oven too long)
= 0.85 × 0.85 × 0.85 × 0.85 × 0.85 × 0.85 = 0.3771... *[1 mark]*
P(Ore leaves at least one cake in the oven too long)
= 1 − 0.3771... = 0.6228... = 0.623 (3 s.f.) *[1 mark]*

3 a) Events A and B are independent,
so P(A and B) = P(A) × P(B) = 0.35 × 0.4 = 0.14
P(A and not B) = 0.35 − 0.14 = 0.21 and
P(B and not A) = 0.4 − 0.14 = 0.26
1 − 0.21 − 0.14 − 0.26 = 0.39 goes outside the circles.
So the Venn diagram looks like this:

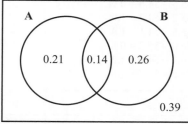

[3 marks available — 1 mark for the correct value in the intersection, 1 mark for the remaining correct values in the circles, 1 mark for the correct value outside the circles]

b) P(A or B) = P(A) + P(B) − P(A and B)
= 0.35 + 0.4 − 0.14 = 0.61
[2 marks available — 1 mark for a correct method, 1 mark for the correct answer]
You could have just added up the values inside the circles here —
0.21 + 0.14 + 0.26 = 0.61.

Page 74: Tree Diagrams

1 a)
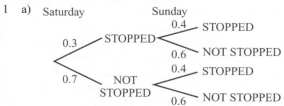

[2 marks available — 1 mark for the first set of branches correct, 1 mark for the second set of branches correct]

b) P(stopped, stopped) = 0.3 × 0.4 = 0.12 *[1 mark]*

c) P(stopped exactly once)
= P(stopped, not stopped) + P(not stopped, stopped)
= (0.3 × 0.6) + (0.7 × 0.4) *[1 mark]* = 0.18 + 0.28
= 0.46 *[1 mark]*

2 a) P(Blues win, Blues win) = 0.2 × 0.2 = 0.04 *[1 mark]*

b) P(the same team wins both matches = P(Blues win, Blues win)
+ P(Greys win, Greys win) = 0.04 + (0.3 × 0.3) = 0.13
[2 marks available — 1 mark for a correct method, 1 mark for the correct answer]

c) P(at least one draw) = P(Greys win, draw) + P(draw, Greys win)
+ P(draw, draw) + P(draw, Blues win) + P(Blues win, draw)
= (0.3 × 0.5) + (0.5 × 0.3) + (0.5 × 0.5)
+ (0.5 × 0.2) + (0.2 × 0.5) = 0.75
[2 marks available — 1 mark for a correct method, 1 mark for the correct answer]
You could have worked out P(no draws) = 0.25
and subtracted this from 1 instead.

Pages 75-76: Conditional Probability

1 a) There are 71 people who prefer pop music, and 30 of those
are male, so P(male | pop music) = $\frac{30}{71}$
[2 marks available — 1 mark for using correct denominator (71), 1 mark for correct answer]

b) There are 120 females, and 48 of those prefer hip-hop, so
P(hip-hop | female) = $\frac{48}{120} = \frac{2}{5}$
[2 marks available — 1 mark for using correct denominator (120), 1 mark for correct answer]

2 a) The first card was a vowel, leaving 7 cards of which 3
are consonants, so P(C | V) = $\frac{3}{7}$
[2 marks available — 1 mark for considering the effects of the first pick, 1 mark for the correct answer]

b)
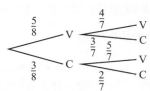

[3 marks available — 1 mark for the first set of branches correct, 1 mark for each of the second set of branches correct]

c) P(2nd Card Vowel) = P(V, V) + P(C, V)
= $\left(\frac{5}{8} \times \frac{4}{7}\right) + \left(\frac{3}{8} \times \frac{5}{7}\right) = \frac{20}{56} + \frac{15}{56} = \frac{35}{56} = \frac{5}{8}$
[2 marks available — 1 mark for a correct method, 1 mark for the correct answer]

d) The number of cards decreases on each pick, so the
denominator decreases by 1 each time. The number of vowels
decreases after each of the first three picks, so the numerators
of the first three fractions decrease by 1 as well. On the fourth
pick, there are still 3 consonants to choose from, as none have
been selected so far. So:
P(V, V, V, C) = $\frac{5}{8} \times \frac{4}{7} \times \frac{3}{6} \times \frac{3}{5} = \frac{3}{28}$
[3 marks available — 1 mark for a correct method, 1 mark for the correct probabilities after each pick, 1 mark for the correct answer]
Be careful here — the probabilities change after each pick because the cards aren't replaced.

3 a) 28 + 12 + 5 + 11 = 56 people watch football, of whom 11 + 5
= 16 also watch cricket. So P(cricket | football) = $\frac{16}{56} = \frac{2}{7}$.
[2 marks available — 1 mark for using correct denominator (56), 1 mark for correct answer]

b) 9 + 12 + 5 + 18 = 44 people watch athletics,
of whom 5 also watch football and cricket.
So P(football and cricket | athletics) = $\frac{5}{44}$
[2 marks available — 1 mark for using correct denominator (44), 1 mark for correct answer]

4 Sketch a tree diagram to help:
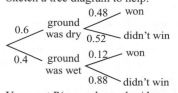

You want P(ground was dry | horse won), so you need to find
P(horse won) and P(horse won and ground was dry).
P(horse won) = (0.6 × 0.48) + (0.4 × 0.12) = 0.336 *[1 mark]*
P(horse won and ground was dry) = 0.6 × 0.48 = 0.288 *[1 mark]*
So P(ground was dry | horse won)
= P(horse won and ground was dry) ÷ P(horse won) *[1 mark]*
= 0.288 ÷ 0.336 = 0.85714... = 0.857 (3 s.f.) *[1 mark]*
Trying to do this one without a tree diagram is tricky — and if you're not sure where 0.48 came from, it's 0.12 × 4 (as Uma's horse is 4 times more likely to win a race if the ground is dry).

5 a) No, the events are not independent — for independent events,
P(A | B) = P(A), but from the information given in the
question, P(A) = 0.35 and P(A | B) = 0.25.
[2 marks available — 1 mark for stating that the events are not independent, 1 mark for a sensible explanation]

b) P(A | B) = $\frac{P(A \text{ and } B)}{P(B)}$,
so P(A and B) = P(A | B) × P(B) = 0.25 × 0.28 = 0.07
[2 marks available — 1 mark for using the formula correctly, 1 mark for the correct answer]

c) P(B | A) = $\frac{P(A \text{ and } B)}{P(A)} = \frac{0.07}{0.35} = 0.2$
[2 marks available — 1 mark for using the formula correctly, 1 mark for the correct answer]

Section Seven — Probability Distributions

Page 77: The Binomial Distribution

1 a) Any one from:
The coin tosses (trials) must be independent. / There are only two possible outcomes (success or failure, i.e. heads or tails). / The number of tosses is fixed ($n = 5$).
[1 mark for any sensible answer]

b) P(not head) = $1 - \frac{1}{3} = \frac{2}{3}$ *[1 mark]*
P(heads at least twice) = 1 – P(1 head or 0 heads) *[1 mark]*
= 1 – P(1 head) – P(0 heads)
P(1 head) = ${}^5C_1 p^1 q^4 = 5 \times \frac{1}{3} \times \left(\frac{2}{3}\right)^4 = 0.3292...$ *[1 mark]*
P(0 heads) = ${}^5C_0 p^0 q^5 = \left(\frac{2}{3}\right)^5 = 0.1316...$ *[1 mark]*
P(heads at least twice) = $1 - 0.3292... - 0.1316... = 0.5390...$
$= 0.539$ (3 d.p.) *[1 mark]*
For any n, ${}^nC_1 = n$ and ${}^nC_0 = 1$.

c) The expected value is np so $4 = np = 5p$ *[1 mark]*
$\Rightarrow p = 0.8$ *[1 mark]*

2 a) $p = 0.65$ *[1 mark]*

b) P(not on time) = $q = 1 - $ P(on time) $= 0.35$ *[1 mark]*
P(3 not on time) = ${}^{10}C_3 \times 0.35^3 \times 0.65^7$ *[1 mark]*
$= 120 \times 0.35^3 \times 0.65^7$
$= 0.2522... = 0.252$ (3 s.f.) *[1 mark]*

c) P(all trains on time) = 0.65^n *[1 mark]* > 0.2
Try different values of n:
$n = 3 \Rightarrow 0.65^n = 0.274...$ (which is greater than 0.2)
$n = 4 \Rightarrow 0.65^n = 0.178...$ (which is not greater than 0.2)
[1 mark]
So the greatest number of trains that can arrive is 3. *[1 mark]*

Page 78: The Normal Distribution

1 a) 95% of the weights should be within 2 standard deviations of the mean. $a = 418 - 2 \times 0.7 = 416.6$ g and $b = 418 + 2 \times 0.7 = 419.4$ g.
[2 marks available — 1 mark for using mean ± 2 s.d., 1 mark for the correct values of a and b]

b) 910 kg = 1000 – 90, i.e. one standard deviation below the mean. You expect 100% – 68% = 32% of the values to be outside one standard deviation of the mean. Since the normal distribution is symmetrical, you expect 32% ÷ 2 = 16% of the values to be below 910 kg. So that's $300 \times 0.16 = 48$ days.
[3 marks available — 1 mark for recognising mean – s.d., 1 mark for using 16%, 1 mark for correct final answer]

2 a) Age in whole years is not continuous and the normal distribution only applies to continuous variables. *[1 mark]*

b) E.g.

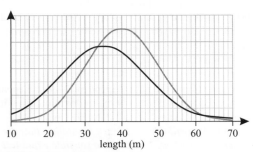

length (m)

[2 marks available — 1 mark for a bell-shaped curve with peak at 35 m, 1 mark for the peak of the curve lower and the spread wider than that of the given curve]

c) $13 = 35 - 2 \times 11$ and $57 = 35 + 2 \times 11$, i.e. two standard deviations below and above the mean *[1 mark]*.
So 95% of the planes should have wingspans between these values *[1 mark]*.
So the probability of selecting such a plane is 0.95 *[1 mark]*.

Pages 79-80: Quality Assurance

1 a) E.g. to ensure the skirts produced are the size that the customer expects. *[1 mark for any sensible reason]*

b) Sample means are more closely distributed than sample values (there's less variation between them). *[1 mark]*

2 a) 13:00 range = 55.5 – 54.6 = 0.9
14:00 range = 55.2 – 54.2 = 1.0
15:00 range = 55.5 – 54.1 = 1.4
16:00 range = 56.0 – 55.2 = 0.8
17:00 range = 56.1 – 54.9 = 1.2
18:00 range = 55.5 – 53.7 = 1.8

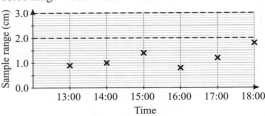

[2 marks available — 1 mark for all sample ranges calculated correctly, 1 mark for all plotted correctly]

b) A sample range is only concerning if it is too high (an ideal sample range would be 0 cm, and you can't have a negative range). *[1 mark]*

c) Yes, it seems to be functioning, as all the sample ranges are below the warning limit. *[1 mark]*

3 a) The region outside 19 - 21 is outside the warning limits. 1 in 20 of the sample means are expected to be outside the warning limits, which is 5%. *[1 mark]*

b) Warning limits are set at 2 standard deviations above and below the target value. Using the upper warning limit:
$21 = 20 + 2\sigma$ *[1 mark]* $\Rightarrow \sigma = 0.5$ *[1 mark]*
You could have done this using the action limits, which are 3 standard deviations above and below the target value — e.g. $21.5 = 20 + 3\sigma \Rightarrow \sigma = 1.5 \div 3 = 0.5$.

c) The machine should be stopped immediately (or the machine should be reset). *[1 mark]*
The mean of the eighth sample was above the action limit.

4 a) $(400.9 + 401.8 + 401.5 + 402.2) \div 4 = 401.6$ g *[1 mark]*

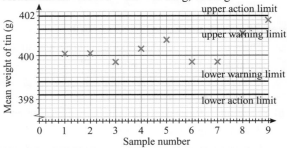

[1 mark]

b) Warning limits: $400 \pm 2 \times 0.6 = 398.8$ g, 401.2 g
Action limits: $400 \pm 3 \times 0.6 = 398.2$ g, 401.8 g

[3 marks available — 1 mark for using 400 ± 2 s.d. for warning limits, 1 mark for using 400 ± 3 s.d. for action limits, 1 mark for all four lines drawn and labelled correctly]

c) The ninth sample is outside the warning limits *[1 mark]* so another sample should be taken at once. If this is also outside the warning limits, production should be stopped. *[1 mark]*

MSXO41

Answers